# ADDICT IN THE FAMILY

# ADDICT IN THE FAMILY

## HOW TO COPE WITH THE LONG HAUL

Dr Andrew Byrne

## A NOTE TO THE READER

While every care has been taken to ensure that the content of this book is accurate, the author and publisher do not accept legal liability for any problems arising from the implementation of the various treatment strategies outlined therein. The high mortality amongst street heroin users means that deaths are occasionally encountered in this field. The aim of this work is to assist family members and others to ease the suffering of those affected by heroin addiction.

*by the same author:*

*"Methadone in the Treatment of Narcotic Addiction"*
*A guide for those involved in prescribing methadone.*

*Available from Tosca Press*

Published by Tosca Press,
75 Redfern Street, Redfern, NSW, Australia, 2016
Telephone 61 2 9319 5524 Facsimile 61 2 9318 0631

© Andrew James Byrne 1996

ISBN 0 646 29144 0

# ADDICT IN THE FAMILY

## HOW TO COPE WITH THE LONG HAUL

---

# CONTENTS

---

This book is dedicated to the many Australian heroin addicts who continue to suffer.  We should endeavour to minimise the harm resulting from drug and alcohol use, especially in the young.  Prohibition of drugs has failed to achieve this goal and policy changes are needed to prevent the continuing tragedy.  Many authorities have adopted the 'harm minimisation' philosophy including the limited availability of certain drugs such as cannabis, methadone and even heroin.  As politicians enact more enlightened legislation, there will be fewer overdoses, less viral disease transmission, crime and other untoward consequences of illicit drug use.

Thanks are due to Rosemary Blayney, Bill Brooks, Allan Gill and Anne Love who all assisted in the preparation of this work.  My father, John Justinian Byrne, has been the guiding light for most of the medical principles espoused in this small book.  He still runs the 'family practice' started by his father, James Michael Byrne, at Ramsgate on Sydney's Botany Bay.

# Introduction

## "DRUGS ARE ALL AROUND US!"

The current wave of illicit drug use in Australia began in the days of the Vietnam War when large numbers of American troops spent rest and recreation leave in our big cities. For five years from 1967 they brought their pent up frustrations from the war zone, their pay packets and their drugs.

It is believed that up to 20% of these young Americans were using heroin regularly. With opium being a traditional crop in adjacent countries, the refined end-product, heroin was also readily available in Vietnam. When going on leave, personnel could purchase sufficient for a week or two. In Australia, heroin was hardly known as a social problem and customs inspections were usually waived for allied military staff.

But these soldiers were not 'junkies'. They were highly trained military staff fighting a war. Their drug was easy to obtain and their salaries were sufficient to cover the cost. For today's addict, just obtaining the drug can be a full time occupation, to the exclusion of normal daily life. For these troops, however, heroin was used more like tobacco.

Interestingly, the majority returned to America and spontaneously ceased using drugs. A small proportion who could not cope with normal civilian life required special services such as residential rehabilitation, detoxification or methadone treatment. For some reason very few Australian service personnel used heroin in Vietnam.

These Americans were called 'R & R' boys, being on rest and recreation leave. While in Australia, they mixed with young sociable singles as well as fringe dwellers, alcoholics and prostitutes. A number of these associates also developed a taste for the new drug. Many began by smoking or 'snorting' the drug. When it is injected, a given quantity of heroin goes a lot further. Intravenous use also gives a transient but intense pleasurable feeling called a 'rush'.

These consumers were mostly habitués of Sydney's Kings Cross and they formed the first substantial market for illicit narcotics in the white Australian community. Opium had been used discretely in the Chinese community for many years and only rarely came to the attention of the authorities.

Hence we can see that part of what makes an addict 'visible' is the illegal nature of their drug-of-choice. The other necessary condition which makes a 'drug user' into an 'addict' is that they become unable or unwilling to cease their drug use.

The popularity of cannabis and amphetamines also increased in the 1960s, while cocaine was still rare in Australia until the 1980s. The market for these drugs has grown to such an extent that they are now larger than many legitimate crops and industries.

We may have difficulty being objective about 'drugs'. Many people regard 'drugs' as the illegal ones, forgetting that tobacco and alcohol are not only more damaging, but also more addictive than some illicit drugs such as cannabis. Many average Australians are also addicted to tranquillizers, but these problems are beyond the scope of this book.

A patient with migraine was asked: "Do you take any drugs?" "Certainly not!" came the offended response. Closer questioning revealed a very different story, however. This woman was a smoker and quite a heavy drinker. She also took laxatives in an effort to lose weight. Apart from over-the-counter pain killers, she was taking the contraceptive pill. She also drank an average of eight cups of brewed coffee per day. And this lady had stated that she did not take drugs!!

Most traditional societies had access to a mood altering substance, be it alcohol, coca leaf, betel nut, peyote cactus, tobacco or coffee. In the modern world, unprecedented choices and unfettered consumerism give us the choice of a variety of 'drugs', sometimes by other names. Our mornings start with tea or coffee. The day is punctuated with 'smoko' breaks which are sanctified into Australian industrial law. Often, sleep is ushered in with a glass of tawny port or another sedative draught.

Our country's first currency was rum. Australia's inherited institution of 'shouting' drinks leaves non-drinkers out in the cold. This peer pressure yields a feeling of 'safety in numbers' despite the risks. People's sense of responsibility diminishes when things are done in concert. This is reflected in such unsavoury events as football riots and other unruly crowd behaviour.

At least half of the most popular items in supermarkets are based on 'drugs'. Tobacco, coffee, tea, cola, paracetamol, aspirin and laxatives are all big business. If we include monosodium glutamate, fluoride, the xanthenes from chocolate and liquorice as drugs, then drug-free mouthfuls would be exceptional indeed! Governments depend heavily upon tax revenue from these luxury items. In Australia, all confectionery, soft drinks, alcohol and tobacco are taxed, in some cases more than once.

The harmful effects from some these substances has been well established scientifically, while for others it is simply unknown. Although some are quite hazardous, some others may be relatively harmless. Tobacco and alcohol have been studied closely. Aspirin is not without its potential for harm, nor are large quantities of caffeine in susceptible people.

We are taught that 'taking drugs is bad', yet drug use goes on all around us. Children perceive this inconsistency at an early age. How do we confront this dilemma in the young?

The answer is to start by being open and honest. 'Yes, we take drugs. Yes, we enjoy taking certain drugs. We know there are risks, just as there are with surfing or hang gliding. We accept those risks and take these drugs within certain constraints'.

This informed freedom of choice is fundamental in a modern society. Only a strange, irrational jurisdiction would again try to ban drugs outright. History clearly demonstrates that the outlawing of popular psychoactive substances is counterproductive and pointless. Coffee, alcohol, cannabis, steroids, heroin and methadone have all been banned at some time, each with untoward, and sometimes tragic consequences. We already know more effective ways of regulating the consumption of these substances. Means such as education, taxation, honest labelling and advertising restrictions are more effective than putting young people in jail for using drugs.

The decriminalisation of prostitution and pornography may have caused an increase in their visibility. However, their actual extent in society probably remains constant. Criminologists have known for years that raising penalties has no effect on the incidence of crime. Even capital punishment has not eliminated heroin related crime as was hoped in some Asian countries. The perceived chance of being detected is the only controllable factor which can alter individual crime rates. After thousands of years of popularity, opioids continue a love-hate relationship with our civilisation.

So, do not be shocked by reality. While it is often stranger than fiction, it is real people who are involved, and they may be very close. We need to use all the humility we can muster, as the next to fall from grace may be our own near and dear, or even ourselves!

⌘

# 1

## FINDING OUT

**REALISATION OF THE FACTS**
**A CLASSIFICATION OF COMMON PSYCHOACTIVE DRUGS**
**WHAT TERMS TO USE AND WHO TO TELL?**
**WHAT CAN I DO TO HELP?**
**DO'S AND DONTS FOR RELATIVES OF DRUG USERS**

**REALISATION OF THE FACTS**

So, you have just found out that a family member or close friend is a heroin addict. It may come as quite a shock. It may also explain a lot of unusual observations over a long period.

This may happen by chance or when suspicious goings on are looked into. After following some initial clues, investigations by a parent or other loved-one may reveal the evidence. This might include the actual drugs or drug-using equipment such as a smoking bong, needle, syringe, tourniquet, sterile water containers or a burned spoon, foils or spent rubber caps. Alternatively, it may occur in the context of a crisis such as an overdose, serious legal charge or the discovery of medical problems such as thrombosis, HIV or hepatitis.

In yet another scenario, the drug user may just come out and say, 'Look, I'm a junkie! Please take me as I am. I am sorry for all the trouble I have caused and I want to give it another try.'

Loved-ones often overlook the evidence of drug use. They may ascribe things to 'a difficult time', nerves, growing pains, work troubles, illness or other more palatable shortcomings.

The discovery of unequivocal proof of drug use may be devastating. Reactions vary from rejection and hostility to even further denial of the problem. With time, patience and understanding, most of these tensions can be overcome and previous harmonious relationships restored and even improved.

The majority of addicts by this stage have deceived people around them and some have committed robberies or other schemes to generate income for drugs. Few of them are proud of it, but some try to justify such behaviour. Society, they say, has placed them in the untenable position of being addicted to a drug which is illegal.

---

### A CLASSIFICATION OF COMMON PSYCHOACTIVE DRUGS

**NARCOTICS (OPIOIDS):**
(common names in brackets)
di-acetyl morphine (heroin)
morphine (MS Contin)
pethidine (US: demerol)
monoacetyl morphine
  ('home-bake')
dextromoramide (Palfium)
oxycodone (Endone)
buprenorphine (Temgesic)
methadone (Physeptone)
pentazocine (Fortral)
propoxyphene (Doloxene)
codeine phosphate
dihydrocodeine
diphenoxylate (Lomotil)
poppy seeds

**HALLUCINOGENS:**
lysergic acid diethylamide
  ('LSD')
magic mushrooms
mescalin (peyote cactus)

**RELAXANTS & DEPRESSANTS:**
alcohol
benzodiazepines
methaqualone, barbiturates
cannabis leaf, hashish resin

**SYMPATHOMIMETIC
  STIMULANTS:**
amphetamine
metamphetamine
methyl phenydate (Ritalin)
methylene dioxymeth-
  amphetamine ('ecstasy')
ephedrine
pseudo-ephedrine

**OTHER STIMULANTS:**
cocaine
crack (free-base cocaine)
nicotine
caffeine
betel nut
coca leaf

A small number of addicts first received narcotics in the context of medical or dental treatment. Finding the medical profession unable to treat their addiction, the may have moved to illicit drugs.

The commonest illicit narcotics in Sydney are heroin and black market methadone. In Western Australia and New Zealand 'homebake' is most commonly found. Raw opium is popular in India while brown impure heroin is found in Russia. In Poland, a codeine based mixture called 'compot' is the most frequently used opioid. For discussion and explanation of individual drug categories, see appendix at the end of this book.

**WHAT TERMS TO USE AND WHO TO TELL?**

It is important not to tell too many people about someone's addiction. Number one, they may not understand, and secondly it may be none of their business. The stigma is very hard to lose with some people who have fixed ideas about addiction. One reason for this is the poor results from previous approaches to treatment with the experience of repeated relapses to drug or alcohol use. Modern enlightened therapy is more likely to result in an integrated patient much earlier than traditional approaches which often emphasise segregation for extended periods.

Doctors use numerous euphemisms for drug addiction. One common term for a heroin addict is an intravenous drug user (IVDU) although this term may also be applied to users of other injected drugs such as amphetamine and cocaine. Other terms used in medical classification are 'nervous disorder', 'substance abuse', 'chemical dependency', 'morphinism' and 'compulsive self medication'. The legal terms 'self administration', 'possession', 'narcotic trafficking', 'personal use', and the like all have certain definitions in different jurisdictions.

The old term 'nervous breakdown' is not a single medical diagnosis, but is used by some to mean a temporary inability to function due to psychiatric illness. Such conditions include depression, obsessive compulsive disorders, schizophrenia, alcoholism and drug addiction. These may have their origins in disorders as varied as migraine, stroke or shingles.

Heroin addicts should always be frank with their own doctor about what drugs they are using. Drug addiction itself is a treatable condition and its complications may also require medical intervention. The physician should know the full drug history, social circumstances and previous interventions. An examination and pathology testing will reveal important information about suitability for treatment, work or travel. It will also help with the prognosis of infectious diseases.

All doctors are familiar with of the nature of narcotic use and its medical consequences. A small number may be unsympathetic and judgemental. Another group will simply be unfamiliar with drug addiction or its treatment since, until recently, this has not been covered in the medical course. Most doctors are open minded and willing to learn. They also have access to drug and alcohol specialist services and will be guided by their advice.

## WHAT CAN I DO TO HELP?

The answer to this question is simpler than it may appear. One should behave exactly as one would on learning of any other serious problem involving a loved one. Just as if the person had diabetes, angina or HIV, it is important not to panic. Try not to judge, even if you have been hurt. The addicted person probably also hurts for previous transgressions. Learn what you can about the condition. When seeking expert help, be aware that this is a field where there are a lot of self-styled 'experts'. Trained addiction specialists are attached to most large hospitals and most psychiatrists are also familiar with this area.

It is often helpful for relatives or loved ones to attend such a specialist, counsellor or self help group together with the addicted person. This gives an important opportunity for associates to assess the nature and quality of the treatment being considered. They can ventilate any misgivings with the parties involved and ask questions. It should also give them confidence in treatment directions and how they can help to assist in these efforts.

There are self-help groups for family members. *Nar-Anon* and *Al-Anon* members' lives have been affected by drugs and alcohol abuse of others. They use each other's experiences to gain strength and resolve by example and faith. While these groups follow abstinence orientated philosophies, there are equally genuine groups supporting 'harm minimisation' philosophies (ie. accepting continued use of drugs in a more controlled manner). Methadone support groups and 'controlled drinking' or smoking are further examples of this.

Help for family members is also to be had from the local doctor. There are also many pharmacists who are familiar with this field. Drug and alcohol counsellors may be found at some community care centres.

It is best for relatives and others who are close to the addict not to offer advice, however tempting it may be. In our effort to understand, it is best to offer support and sympathy, even when these do not come readily. If circumstances are such that this is not possible at the time, it is best to be frank about one's feelings, but still to leave the way open for future reconciliation.

Do not worsen the situation by giving money which could be used for drugs. If possible, offer assistance with transport, bills or arrangements which are documented to be for treatment purposes, and always pay by non-negotiable cheque or credit card authority.

Do not be enticed into debates about whether abstinence is the best philosophy. Each type of treatment is 'correct' for the right person at the right time. Equally unrewarding are arguments about why someone originally used drugs or what made them relapse on this occasion.

## DO'S AND DONTS FOR RELATIVES OF DRUG USERS

> ### *HOW TO HELP A HEROIN ADDICT IN THE FAMILY*
>
> | "DO" | "DO NOT" |
> |------|----------|
> | Offer sympathy and support | Do not panic or pity |
> | Assist with housing and bills | Do not give cash to the addict |
> | Be honest about prejudices | Do not judge morally |
> | Seek expert advice | Do not set unrealistic goals |
> | Consult others 'in recovery' | Do not cut off dialogue |
> | Assist with chosen treatment | Do not influence treatment type |

⌘

# 2

## "BUT WHY?"

**REASONS FOR DRUG USE
WHO IS <u>NOT</u> A DRUG ADDICT?  PREVENTION
IS IT A DISEASE?  PREDISPOSITION: GENES & ENVIRONMENT
ENZYMES, TOLERANCE AND RECRUITMENT
INITIAL DRUG USE.  WHO ARE THE PUSHERS?
GATEWAY OR STEPPING-STONE MYTHS**

**REASONS FOR DRUG USE**

Why one person becomes an addict and another does not is a fascinating but frustrating question.  It is posed by parents, friends, psychologists, doctors and journalists.  But most of all the question is asked by addicts themselves.

*"Where did we go wrong?"*  *"Why me?"*  *"Why my wife* (or husband, or son or daughter)*?"*  These questions are never satisfactorily answered but there are lots of interesting theories.  For someone with an established addiction, these questions are academic.  Addiction happens.  Addicts come from all walks of life.  There are certain racial differences.  Some addictions are more common in one sex or the other, but no group is immune.

Most drug users simply say that heroin makes them feel good.  They used it first because it was there and they come back for more because they liked the effects.

Why do some 'nice' people become smokers?  Tobacco is a 'dirtier' drug in many ways than narcotics or cannabis.  But smokers are all around us.  Advertising is still seen and this toxin is freely available.  'Nice' people also sometimes become gamblers, they get fat, they drink and smoke and some even use heroin.  The theory that there are predisposed personalities for people with these vices has never been established.  People from all strata of society are afflicted by all of these compulsive disorders.

### WHO IS <u>NOT</u> A DRUG ADDICT?  PREVENTION
This book is primarily concerned with the young adult who is using heroin on a daily basis.  The term 'drug addict' is sometimes used for those using amphetamine, cocaine, tranquillizers or combinations of these drugs.

Just because a teenager uses cannabis occasionally or takes an ecstasy tablet does not mean they are destined to turn into a heroin addict.  The vast majority of such young people never develop a problem with drugs at all.  From the medical point of view it is probably more worrying to find that one's child is smoking tobacco than to learn of occasional cannabis use.

Some coffee, tobacco and alcohol consumers could be termed addicts, the only difference being the legal nature of their drug-of-choice.  Whether legal or illegal, most adults use a variety of drugs in a controlled way and only a minority get into difficulties.

There is virtually nothing a parent can do to prevent a child being exposed to drugs.  What we *can* do is to make sure that our children are equipped with the knowledge to prevent death and disease should they decide to try drugs.  Honest and frank education is the basis for sensible decision making, whether in the field of drug use or other areas such as sex, diet or exercise.

### IS IT A DISEASE?  PREDISPOSITION: GENES & ENVIRONMENT
Another interesting debate is whether drug addiction is a disease.  This argument can go on forever.  The answer lies in the definition of a disease, the definition of addiction as well as the individual's personal attitude towards their drug use.  Debate

of this kind is unproductive, like the unresolvable issue of calling a drug user a client or a patient. It is not worth the energy.

What *can* be said is that drug use can lead to serious medical complications and death. Medical treatment and public health measures *can* favourably influence some of these consequences. And like many other human conditions, it *can* relapse and there is no simple 'cure' as such.

As with obesity, anxiety, hair loss or acne, drug use can be regarded as a normal part of the human condition at one end of the spectrum, but at a certain point, these conditions could also be given a disease designation. It should be up to the individual drug user to decide if this point has been reached, and therefore, whether they wish to be considered as a 'patient' with a medical problem.

Most professionals who work with addicts are struck by the variety of different types of individuals who are affected. Once the addiction is established, studies of the personalities of drug addicts show some common threads. This should come as no surprise as the lifestyle of illicit drug abuse necessitates haste, efficiency and deception, while these in turn breed impatience, apparent avarice and a general lack of reliability. Whether some of these predate the addiction has not been demonstrated. Similarly, studies of the pre-existing characteristics of alcoholics, smokers and compulsive gamblers also reveal an admixture of otherwise average citizens.

Another factor to take into account is that the high mortality in drug addicts may cause selection of the 'fittest' while some less well equipped for the lifestyle may fall by the wayside. Certainly there are some long-time survivors of many years of street drug use. They are remarkable and resourceful people, many of whom could write a riveting life history.

Up to 50% of heroin addicts have a first order relative with an opioid problem. This could be explained on the basis of environment, genetic make-up or a combination of both. Current research favours the latter. There are few families which are not affected by addiction of some sort.

China has 10% of the world's adults but its citizens smoke 30% of the world's tobacco. This country also had an enormous consumption of opium in the nineteenth century. By contrast, it is sometimes stated that Asians share with Jews a low incidence of alcoholism. How much of this is due to genetics and how much to environment is still unclear.

## ENZYMES, TOLERANCE AND RECRUITMENT

Alcohol is the simplest substance abused by humans. Theories about alcoholism may apply to other drugs although differences occur with the more complex pathways of metabolism for other drugs.

There is evidence that some races lack enzyme pathways for metabolising lactose. Similar deficiencies are thought to occur for alcohol metabolism pathways. Without adequate levels of alcohol dehydrogenase and other enzymes, the first steps in alcohol breakdown are stopped. The build up of certain toxic products may then cause the so-called 'Antabuse' reaction including sweating, shakes, nausea and vomiting in those affected.

One theory states that certain of these breakdown products increase in some alcoholics as they drink. They respond by drinking more to avoid the unpleasant effects. Eventually, they become stuporous from alcohol toxicity.

The concept of 'tolerance' explains why more drug is required to obtain the same response with time. This phenomenon applies equally to tobacco, alcohol, heroin and amphetamine. It is caused by a combination of metabolism, 'neuro-adaptation' and learned behaviour. This results in the user increasing quantities of the drug used until a certain plateau level is reached.

The user who has not used drugs for some time is in a situation of great risk. Such people can be dangerously overdosed on comparatively small doses of drugs because their tolerance has diminished. This can happen in less than a week of abstinence with short acting drugs such as heroin.

Certain groups of drugs share 'cross-tolerance' between members. Examples are heroin and methadone; alcohol and benzodiazepine tranquillizers. Use is made of this effect in the medical use of certain drugs to block withdrawal effects of a related substance.

The concept of chemical 'recruitment' is also fundamental to all addictions. This refers to the observation that, following periods of abstinence, relapsing addicts often rapidly return to previous levels of drug use. Although it may have taken many months or even years to develop an addiction initially, subsequent periods may involve a full blown habit within a week or so.

Therefore, an ex-smoker who used to smoke 25 cigarettes daily is very likely to quickly return to the same levels when taking up the habit again. This 'recruitment' principle may also explain why a change to tobacco with a lower nicotine content often causes an increase in the number of cigarettes smoked per day. The old medical concept of 'blockade dosage' of maintenance drugs may also touch on this, but we are into the realm of speculation again. More research is needed in this area.

### INITIAL DRUG USE.  WHO ARE THE PUSHERS?

Hypothetical question: 'How did you get your first taste for gambling (or sex, or beer, or Vegemite, or nail biting)?'

Unfair, perhaps?

Many taste, some reject, others come back occasionally for more and a number get caught up in a big way. These latter are the most visible consumers who are addicted to whatever it may be.

While many addicts express embarrassment and regret over their drug use, some of them express pride in their activities. There are examples of this approach in other areas of human activity. Don Giovanni boasts of over one thousand women he has seduced. Shakespeare's Falstaff tells of the gallons of ale he has consumed. Other stories of big gambling wins, the 'fish that got away' and the like are tall tales of the would-have-been, could-have-been, all recounted with gusto and exaggeration.

The commonest reason that drug users give for their first drug experience is that 'it was there'. Like 'the mountain' in need of being climbed, the very existence of the drug in one's proximity makes it an option. Then a small window of interest turns into an irreversible moment.

More important, and instructive, are the descriptions of what the subjects experienced from this first episode of drug use. They often describe a sense of relaxation, calmness, confidence, energy or exhilaration which was previously unknown. A number describe it as the first time they have ever slept soundly. It was almost as if it were curing some illness that they had.

But often the initial heroin experience is not totally pleasurable. Some people recount severe symptoms of vomiting, sweating and passing out. Smoking also causes coughing and spluttering initially, but these undesirable symptoms do not always dissuade the user from further experimentation. Such symptoms usually subside as the acquired taste takes over.

The second episode of drug use may occasionally be delayed for a number of years after the first 'taste' of narcotics. It may then be some time further on that the subject becomes addicted to the drug.

For those who do become addicted, it is usually a matter of days or weeks to the second episode of drug use, and less than twelve months to the point of addiction. Once the decision is made to use heroin, some describe a full-on quest which occupies their entire being until 'fulfilment' in drug use. But not everyone who tries heroin becomes an addict.

It is often said that 'every user is a dealer' and 'every dealer is a user'. There is some truth to this since the majority of users having been involved in distribution at some point. Equally, a majority in the drug trade are also heroin users themselves.

Some heroin users prefer to buy from dealers who are not users themselves since they think that they are less likely to adulterate the drug for their own needs. Some such dealers subsequently develop a predilection for the substances they deal in, and become addicted themselves. It is harder to be sympathetic towards such individuals. It would, however, be unduly judgemental to say that individuals 'deserve' their addiction.

So, who are the real 'pushers' for tobacco, alcohol and other drugs? The growers, manufacturers, marketers, other smokers (through peer pressure) or even doctors in the old days. In fact none of these is the single major factor. The main 'pusher' is the drug itself. It sells itself and creates its own market.

Tobacco companies claim that their advertising is not aimed to increase overall consumption, but at increasing market share for their own brands. While this is an expedient argument, advertising clearly aims to place smoking as a normal and desirable part of society, with which most veteran smokers would disagree. No-one could honourably recommended a habit which kills over 50% of its consumers!

## GATEWAY OR STEPPING-STONE MYTHS

Although some people consider certain drugs to be 'gateways' to others, scientific evidence is lacking. The concept of 'gateway drugs' is not accepted by most medical authorities. It may even be a fiction invented by latter-day prohibitionists.

It has never been shown that any single drug leads to, or gives a taste for another drug. Some people argue that if cannabis were harder to obtain, then young people would not want to use heroin. Although superficially attractive, this theory is fundamentally flawed. It ignores the fact that it is impossible to eliminate either cannabis or heroin. It also is countered by the fact that the vast majority of those who smoke cannabis never even try narcotics, let alone become addicted.

It is a common scenario for a drug user to commence with alcohol and tobacco use, then to progress to cannabis, amphetamine or cocaine and on to heroin. However, this does not give tobacco or any other substance the distinction of being a 'gateway' drug. We can debunk the 'gateway' theory as being of no relevance to either treatment or policy.

The only arguable progression in drug use is not metabolic, but is demonstrated by those who first use heroin when their cannabis dealer runs out of 'soft drug' supplies. By placing both cannabis and heroin in the same illicit category, governments have unwittingly yielded control to drug dealers who do not distinguish between different drugs. Hence it may well be that if cannabis were more easy to obtain that *fewer* young people would try heroin.

⌘

# 3

# "CAN'T YOU JUST GIVE UP OR SOMETHING?"

**DEFINITION OF ADDICTION - DRUG AND SUBJECT**
**FORMAL PROHIBITION AND LEGAL CONSEQUENCES**
**PRISON CULTURE**
**WHAT DO HEROIN ADDICTS ACTUALLY DO?**
**WHY DON'T ADDICTS GIVE UP?**
**ADDICT CHARACTERISTICS**
**HARMFUL MEDICAL CONSEQUENCES OF OPIOID USE**

**DEFINITION OF ADDICTION - DRUG AND SUBJECT**

A common question is: "Is it the drug, the person, or the circumstances?" In most, the answer is a combination of the three factors.

The majority of addicted Vietnam veterans spontaneously ceased drug use on their return to the US. These were slightly unusual circumstances of drug use. In the war zone, heroin use was associated with enduring hardship, uncertainty and constant risks of death and injury without the support of home and family.

Addictive substances are usually defined by their ability to be associated with continued, compulsive use despite evident adverse consequences, *as well as* the occurrence of reproducible, objective signs of withdrawal when the use of the substance is curtailed. Other features of addiction are 'salience' and 'tolerance'. Salience implies a pre-occupation with the drug and a narrowing of the drug use repertoire. Tolerance may cause the quantities consumed to increase substantially without a corresponding increase in the effects.

As the addiction becomes more entrenched, so the variety of drugs taken becomes more limited and the circumstances of drug use become more regular and predictable. There are close behavioural similarities between the commonplace routine of the morning cup of coffee, cigarette and the daily dose of methadone (or heroin). The major difference health-wise is that the tobacco yields the greater measurable harm of these three addictive drug groups.

Some drugs appear to have relatively minor or no direct adverse consequences in most users, but can cause serious problems in a small number. Stimulants such as coffee, tea, and coca leaf may fall into this category. The moderate or occasional use of cannabis also causes minor adverse medical consequences in most users. These drugs *do* cause *some* degree of harm, but it is difficult to detect either due to its subtlety or to the small proportions of those affected.

## FORMAL PROHIBITION AND LEGAL CONSEQUENCES

In many cases, the most significant adverse consequences come not from the drug directly, but from its prohibition and the consequent high black market price. Being arrested for driving under the influence of alcohol is a major calamity for the individual. Being caught with a quantity of cannabis is also unpleasant.

Many attempts have been made to outlaw drugs and drug importation. These have usually been a knee jerk reaction to a new perceived threat. None has succeeded in significantly halting the progression of drug or alcohol use, which has followed irregular patterns of ebb and flow, rather like tastes in clothing or music.

Coffee was banned by the Sultan of Turkey in the sixteenth century. King George also tried to prevent the 'evils' of English coffee houses, which reopened by popular demand within days of the bans. America's Eighteenth Constitutional

Amendment, or prohibition has been dubbed the world's 'largest social experiment'. It was also a tragic failure. Similarly, despite prohibition, heroin comes into Australasia in immense quantities, mostly from Asian ports.

Importation was successfully impeded for a time in Western Australia and New Zealand. In both these regions, addicts made their own heroin substitute, 'homebake', in mobile factories. Using codeine-containing pain killers as raw material, they produced high potency mono-acetyl morphine which is just as addictive as heroin.

The futility of prohibition applies not only to drugs. Other areas of human behaviour have been subjected to bans. What may be considered normal facets of life by their devotees, may be seen as compulsive, seditious, antisocial habits by critics. Certain religious observances, homosexual behaviour, prostitution, abortion, money lending, gambling and even hanging out washing on Sundays have all been outlawed at times.

The most common police charges against drug users relate to 'possession' and 'self administration' of restricted substances, along with property crimes or stealing. Although these often go together, the former are victimless crimes while the latter are serious breaches of other citizen's rights.

Some magistrates view the self administration or possession of small quantities of illicit drugs as trivial offences, but when in combination with other property crime, they will rightly ask if this person has a problem and if they are doing anything about it. By the time of facing court, weeks or months may have elapsed since the alleged offences. If the accused can produce evidence that they have an addiction problem and that they have commenced some form of treatment, then adjournment or acquittal is more likely. Leniency in sentencing may also involve a bond or condition that the person remain under certain treatment or supervision.

Drug users are also commonly charged with traffic infringements, tenancy violations and minor fraud. These often relate to lack of money and unpaid debts including driver's licence renewal. Court hearings may stay proceedings if debts and drug problems are being attended to and strict schedules of repayment are instituted.

Equally serious are cases of borrowing or stealing from other family members when the police may not have been involved. Families are often slow to realise that cash is nearly always converted into drugs by unstable addicts. Any debt payment on behalf of the out-of-control addict should be in the form of a non-negotiable bank draft. If substantial cash sums are requested the purpose may not be legitimate.

It is difficult for non-addicted people to imagine themselves into the shoes of someone with a compulsive drug use disorder. This is especially so when the affected person is a relative or loved one. Denial is common, even when the evidence may be convincing to those outside the family.

More serious crimes committed by addicts may involve the importation of drugs, dealing in drugs, major fraud and armed robbery. The courts are not lenient in such cases and long prison sentences are usual.

## PRISON CULTURE

Drug use in jails is common. As in the wider community, prohibition cannot succeed in a humane prison. Contact visits, compassionate leave, work release, corrupt contractors or officials all go to ensure that there is a steady supply of drugs for those with the desire to use them and the means to pay.

This is not to say that every prisoner uses drugs regularly. Many see prison as 'time out' from drug use. Indeed, for some drug addicts and alcoholics it is a welcomed reprieve from compulsive and harmful drug use. Whilst in custody, they can get fit, put on weight and attend to important medical and dental problems. The fittest looking drug addict is often just out of jail.

Prison authorities have found that the provision of methadone reduces tensions amongst inmates. Despite initial reservations, it has also been welcomed by warders, medical staff and public health services. Some jails permit condoms but the spread of viral disease is still a major concern. The prison population has higher rates of HIV and hepatitis than the general community. There are also increased risks of spread both within the jail and then to the wider community when prisoners return to their families. The majority of inmates only spend short periods in custody.

## WHAT DO HEROIN ADDICTS ACTUALLY DO?

The majority of heroin addicts who come to the attention of treatment services have been injecting at least twice daily for over six months. Like pathology collectors and the blood bank, intravenous drug users generally employ the most accessible veins. The cubital veins are in the fold of the elbow joint, one being on the outer aspect (lateral) and one on the inner (medial cubital vein). Some also inject into veins of the forearm or hand. Groin, leg, armpit and neck veins are less commonly used in this country. Eyeball and toe veins are fictitious folklore.

A tourniquet is used on the upper arm to block the venous return, making the vein swell. This can be done with a piece of rubber, cord or a neck tie. Once the vein is engorged with blood, it is relatively simple to insert the hypodermic needle into it. To be sure the needle is in the vein, a brief withdrawal of the plunger will show a 'flush' of dark, venous blood. The tourniquet is then released at the same moment as the fluid is injected into the vein.

From the cubital and axillary veins, the drug passes to the right atrium of the heart, then through the lungs to the left atrium and ventricle, aorta and on up to the brain where it has its effect within half a minute. As it passes into the arteries supplying the tongue just before it reaches the brain, the user notices a distinct 'taste' a moment before the euphoric effect. For this reason, the word 'taste' is commonly used in the drug sub-cultures and is synonymous with drug injecting.

Heroin use is often a solitary experience, but some use in groups for protection. In case of accidental overdose, someone will be available to summon help. Groups may also form when a number of addicts are waiting to 'score' a deal of heroin. When the dealer arrives, some clients may be in withdrawal and will want to use the drug as soon as possible. This group is sometimes the extent of the addict's companionship.

With syringes being hard to obtain in some areas, this tragically often meant these groups shared equipment, causing the spread of viral infections such as HIV and hepatitis C.

Although often a lonesome pursuit in our society, in other areas, such as parts of India and Asia, there is a particular social ritual to traditional opium use. This may cross social and religious barriers and is associated with few of the harmful consequences of intravenous use.

## WHY DON'T ADDICTS GIVE UP?

Many addicts *do* stop using drugs. They perceive the dangers, realise their situation and call on their resources to curtail opiate use. Numerous surveys and censuses have found that surprisingly large numbers of Australians have tried illicit opioids, but estimates of the numbers who have been addicted are substantially lower. Despite the obvious severe consequences which occur, some addicts continue to use the drug in a compulsive and harmful manner. These people give various reasons for their behaviour, just like smokers who cannot give up.

'Yes, I would like to give up, but I get so sick when I stop heroin that I would rather die.' 'Yes, I would like to stop, but I would lose my job and there is nobody to look after my children while I went through the withdrawals.' Occasionally, one meets a user who states frankly: 'No, I do not want to give up. Heroin makes me feel good. It gives me energy to go out and do a day's work and helps me relax in the evenings. I pay for it myself and I do not cause anyone else any trouble.' It is difficult to argue against such assertions from informed adults.

Timing is important, and, like smokers, some heroin addicts use drugs for over ten years before deciding that the dangers outweigh the benefits. Other important factors may be the death of a relative or friend, pregnancy, paternity, travel, work and business responsibilities. Religious conversion may also be associated with cessation of illicit drug use.

## ADDICT CHARACTERISTICS
While addicts come from all backgrounds, there are some common characteristics which might constitute 'addict behaviour'. These features come partly from the drug, partly from its illegal status as well as from the subjects themselves.

Despite publicity to the contrary, it is now known that the majority of heroin users are private individuals who spend their own money on their drug-of-choice. They use it unhurriedly in private with clean injecting equipment. The more stereotyped drug users finance their drugs from crime. They use in haste in unsavoury surroundings. They are likely to be unwashed, badly groomed and ill-clad. The latter account for about three quarters of those coming into treatment, but probably less than a quarter of heroin users overall. They are, however, the most visible ones and are often unemployed with little or no social supports. They are more likely to have a police record and to have medical complications of drug use.

Although numerous heroin users never come to the attention of treatment services, those who need treatment have often had a history of continuous daily heroin use. There are about twice as many males as females in treatment. New patients are most often in their mid to late twenties but they may be as old as fifty.

Most heroin users have tried to give up narcotics, and many have succeeded for substantial periods. Others consciously limit their heroin use at certain times for their own reasons.

## HARMFUL MEDICAL CONSEQUENCES OF OPIOID USE
A view is often stated that pure heroin is harmless. While no intravenous drug is 'harmless', there is some truth to this adage. Unlike alcohol or tobacco, heroin causes no on-going toxicity to the tissues or organs of the body. Apart from causing

some constipation, it appears to have no side effects in most who take it. When administered safely, its use may be consistent with a long and productive life. The principal harm comes from the risk of overdose, problems with injecting, drug impurities and adverse legal or financial consequences. Injected heroin can never be 'safe' when the exact dose is unknown. A lethal dose of narcotic may be as little as 50% above the standard or average dose.

Apart from sedation, rare but well documented side effects of narcotics include dry mouth, sexual abnormalities, growth of breast tissue in males, menstrual irregularities in women and excessive sweating. These can occur with all opioids such as codeine, morphine, heroin and methadone. The symptoms are usually mild and self-limited, but occasionally they may be trigger factors inducing addicts to curtail their drug intake.

⌘

# 4

---

# "... OR SOMETHING" - TREATMENT OPTIONS

---

**ABSTINENCE ORIENTATED TREATMENTS**
**DETOXIFICATION**
**NARCOTICS ANONYMOUS**
**THERAPEUTIC COMMUNITIES**
**ALTERNATIVES TO ABSTINENCE**
**METHADONE MAINTENANCE TREATMENT**
**WHAT HAPPENS WHEN COMMENCING METHADONE?**
**'PROBLEMS' WITH METHADONE**
**METHADONE: RESEARCH AND MYTHS**
**PRESCRIBED HEROIN AND OTHER OPIOIDS**

## ABSTINENCE ORIENTATED TREATMENTS

A number of addicts are able to recognise the problem and do something about it. Some move to the country for a spell. This is called a 'geographical'. And it sometimes works. Other times, however, when the person returns to familiar surroundings, they also return to old habits.

Another method is to go into a detoxification ('detox') unit where there are like-minded people, a comfortable bed and supportive environment to face the symptoms of withdrawal. This usually takes five to ten days in the case of heroin or alcohol. Withdrawals from long-acting drugs such as tranquillizers or methadone may take more than a month.

When necessary, most addicts can wean themselves down to a low dose of their drug-of-choice. From this point some can spontaneously cease drug use altogether. However, given the circumstances, many will return to drug use unless some protective mechanism has been set in place.

Hence it is important not only to obtain sobriety, but to maintain it by using any means possible. One common method is for the addict to hand over responsibility for their finances to someone else such as a spouse. Another effective strategy to avoid a return to drug use is participation in a formal self-help program such as *Narcotics Anonymous*.

# TREATMENT OPTIONS:

☞   HOME DETOXIFICATION

☞   CLINIC DETOXIFICATION

☞   'GEOGRAPHICAL' DETOXIFICATION

☞   MEDICATED DETOXIFICATION

☞   NARCOTICS ANONYMOUS

☞   THERAPEUTIC COMMUNITY
     = RESIDENTIAL 'REHAB'

☞   METHADONE MAINTENANCE

☞   METHADONE REDUCTIONS

☞   OTHER OPIOID PRESCRIPTION

☞   PRESCRIBED HEROIN

☞   NALTREXONE

## DETOXIFICATION

Formal 'drying out' can be accomplished in the hospital or hostel environment. The supports provided vary according to the principles followed by each establishment. Most however, connect with a *Twelve Step* or *Narcotics Anonymous* (NA) program for those who are so inclined. This involves utilising the 'pain' of drugs as a 'gain' towards abstinence, and is highly successful for a proportion of addicts.

Numerous patients have been helped to detoxify at home by family members. Some may be new to the process and are often unsupported by outside services. Occasionally, the addict's family members are so affected by their loved-one's appearance, that they buy some heroin to relieve their relative's suffering. This, of course, is counter productive, and it puts an enormous responsibility onto those involved. They would be well advised to consult medical and self-help services during this difficult time. Some institutions will even supervise and medicate an out-patient detoxification program at the patient's home. The local doctor may also be involved.

It is almost impossible to quit two habits at the same time without support. For those with multiple addictions, such as heroin, nicotine and tranquillizers, home detoxification is inappropriate. It is preferable for the patient to be admitted to a detoxification ward for supervision of this complex process.

There are two types of in-patient detoxification, medicated and non-medicated. The medicated variety may use narcotics or non-narcotics to cushion the unpleasant symptoms of withdrawal. It should be understood, however, that the use of any narcotic drug during this process will usually lengthen it. Hence many addicts and carers believe that it is best to use no drugs at all.

The main problem during this period is lack of sleep. Some recovering addicts state that it took six months before they had a normal night's sleep after stopping drugs. Unfortunately, sleeping tablets are not appropriate for these people. Such medications are generally from the benzodiazepine family of drugs which are all addictive. Such tranquillizers can be more harmful than narcotics. This is especially so when they are taken in high doses or when they are used over long periods of time, even at recommended doses. Useful non-drug methods of treating withdrawals include massage, hot baths and other physical manoeuvres.

Apart from insomnia, the usual accompaniments of *detox* from narcotics are *depression, debility* (fatigue), *diarrhoea* and *dolor* (Greek for pain). Some are troubled by backache, headaches, or abdominal pains which must be distinguished from medical or surgical causes. These always wane with time, as long as the subject remains drug-free. Fits do not occur from narcotic withdrawals, but are regularly seen with those who have abused tranquillizers or alcohol.

There is little relation between the quantity of drug habit, the length of time drugs were used and the severity of symptoms in withdrawal. Some addicts describe symptoms similar to a mild influenza, while others used superlatives and expletives to emphasise their suffering.

Non-narcotic drugs which have been recommended for these symptoms are paracetamol, clonidine, lofexidine and various vitamin combinations. None of these is dramatically effective. The long acting tranquillizer, diazepam (Valium) is used sparingly in many detox units for the first night or two. A synthetic narcotic, propoxyphene (Doloxene) is also occasionally used.

**NARCOTICS ANONYMOUS**
Each 'member' attends a meeting of recovering addicts. The only condition for acceptance is a desire to stop using drugs. At the gathering it is possible to simply be an observer, while active members will recite their story out-loud to the group. New members are encouraged to share what they are going through. Some find that they need to attend meetings daily at first. Since most groups meet weekly, this means going to several different groups for a time. Continuity is kept by a

'sponsor' who can share day to day stresses by being available in person or by telephone when needed. There are no fees and no coercion.

*Narcotics Anonymous* is an effective strategy for avoiding drugs after the detoxification period is over. As with dieting, quitting cigarettes or other significant behavioural modifications, it is the 'long haul' which really matters for favourable outcomes. People who develop problems with excessive cannabis use often identify well with AA groups.

There are many different self-help societies in Australia dealing with a multitude of behavioural problems using variations of the *Twelve Step* program. Pills Anonymous, Gamblers, Shop-lifters, Hand Washers etc. all have one thing in common. They accept the existence of their compulsive behaviour as a disease over which they have no control except to avoid the trigger factor completely. This is easy to define in terms of drug or alcohol use. For other behavioural disturbances, there may be some difficulty in determining where ordinary behaviour becomes pleasurable, stress-relieving or compulsive.

There are many sensible principles expounded by AA and NA which can be useful for those who are not actively participating in such programs. Such folklore includes the following:

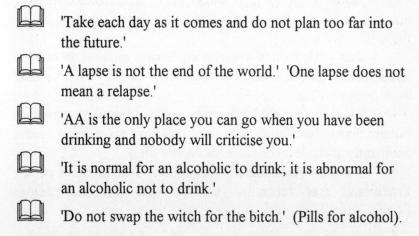

    📖    'Take each day as it comes and do not plan too far into the future.'

    📖    'A lapse is not the end of the world.' 'One lapse does not mean a relapse.'

    📖    'AA is the only place you can go when you have been drinking and nobody will criticise you.'

    📖    'It is normal for an alcoholic to drink; it is abnormal for an alcoholic not to drink.'

    📖    'Do not swap the witch for the bitch.' (Pills for alcohol).

## THE TWELVE TRADITIONS*

**One** - Our common welfare should come first; personal recovery depends upon A.A. unity.

**Two** - For our group purpose there is but one ultimate authority - a loving God as He may express Himself in our group conscience. Our leaders are but trusted servants; they do not govern.

**Three** - The only requirement for A.A. membership is a desire to stop drinking.

**Four** - Each group should be autonomous except in matters affecting other groups or A.A. as a whole.

**Five** - Each group has but one primary purpose - to carry its message to the alcoholic who still suffers.

**Six** - An A.A. group ought never endorse, finance or lend the A.A. name to any related facility or outside enterprise, lest problems of money, property and prestige divert us from our primary purpose.

**Seven** - Every A.A. group ought to be fully self-supporting, declining outside contributions.

**Eight** - Alcoholics Anonymous should remain forever nonprofessional, but our service centers may employ special workers.

**Nine** - A.A., as such, ought never be organized; but we may create service boards or committees directly responsible to those they serve.

**Ten** - Alcoholics Anonymous has no opinion on outside issues; hence the A.A. name ought never be drawn into public controversy.

**Eleven** - Our public relations policy is based on attraction rather than promotion; we need always maintain personal anonymity at the level of press, radio and films.

**Twelve** - Anonymity is the spiritual foundation of all our Traditions, ever reminding us to place principles before personalities.

[*taken from Alcoholics Anonymous, 1939, AA World Services.]

## THERAPEUTIC COMMUNITIES

The 'therapeutic community' or 'residential rehab' is a traditional form of medium to long term treatment for drug (usually heroin) addicts. They enter a residential complex which is often in the country. Part of the treatment is a complete separation from previous lifestyle, associates and work. Even family visits are strictly limited as segregation is integral to the philosophy.

After up to twelve months in this regimented environment the 'recovering addicts' graduate to a 'half-way' or 'safe' house in town. From here, trips out are only permitted when accompanied by other members to prevent relapse to drug use. As time goes on, solo visits are allowed as members rejoin normal society, resume education or gain employment.

For unselected patients the success rate of therapeutic communities is quite low. Those sent by court order to be admitted to such establishments are extremely unlikely to remain free of drugs for long periods. Even medium-term successes may be as low as 10%. This form of treatment is also expensive as it involves residential care over long periods. On the other hand, in well motivated and self-selected addicts, the success rates are substantially better.

It would be impossible to accommodate the estimated 100,000 Australian addicts in this form of treatment. Other means must be used for the majority of heroin users in need of treatment.

## ALTERNATIVES TO ABSTINENCE

Although there are many valid approaches, the fundamentals in the area of drug addiction have been known for many years. There are some parallels between the treatment of alcoholism, smoking and heroin addiction. When choosing the type of treatment which is best for a particular addict, one must be unemotional and objective since what suits one may not suit another. In treating addictions, one type of treatment may be unsatisfactory the first time around but may be successful on the next occasion. This should not mean, however, that unsuccessful treatments should be repeated time after time when there are alternatives.

A very small number of addicts may benefit from medical prescription of specific 'antagonists'. Disulfiram tablets ('Antabuse' for alcoholism) and naltrexone treatment (for narcotic addiction and sometimes alcoholism) can help maintain sobriety once this has been achieved. These antagonist drugs are most effective when used under the supervision of a third party such as a family member or pharmacist. Despite its reported successes in treating both narcotic addiction and alcoholism overseas, Australian authorities have not yet licensed naltrexone for general use.

When other methods have been tried and failed, an alternative is to give maintenance doses of a safe 'agonist' drug. Alcoholics in withdrawal can be given tranquillizers temporarily (usually Valium) to prevent or delay the onset of withdrawal symptoms, including fits. Even alcohol itself has been given in certain situations where the likelihood of abstinence is low. This may occur when a heavy drinker needs hospitalisation for an injury, illness or operation. Such treatment is not successful in the long term treatment of alcoholism, although some alcoholics do trade one addiction for another.

Acceptance of continued use of intoxicants runs counter to the principles of *Narcotics Anonymous*. However, it does accept the subject's dependence and may involve a desire for a longer term abstinence. This might be called 'Step Zero' and is equivalent to the 'pre-contemplation' phase of tobacco quitters.

## METHADONE MAINTENANCE TREATMENT

The use of methadone as a treatment for illicit opioid use is now widespread and highly successful. Methadone is an opiate drug with some of the same properties as heroin. Like heroin, methadone has a very low incidence of tissue or organ damage in humans. Unlike heroin, methadone is very long acting, and is best absorbed orally.

Like heroin itself 50 years earlier, methadone was first marketed by a German drug company. World War II made traditional middle eastern sources uncertain, so synthetic opioids were being sought.

Oral absorption of methadone is nearly one hundred percent while the 'half-life' is between 24 and 60 hours. Once-daily administration of an *appropriate individual dose* will abolish withdrawal symptoms without inducing euphoria.

The use of methadone in addiction treatment was first reported by Dr Vincent P. Dole in New York in 1963[1]. He and his psychiatrist wife, Marie Nyswander, had both observed the poor results of traditional treatment of addictions. As a biochemical researcher in New York he witnessed the scene at the 125th Street Railroad Station. In the 1950s, Dr Nyswander had written a book about heroin addiction being a medical disease, worthy of more attention from doctors. They were both convinced that the extraordinary plight of heroin addicts must be due to metabolic factors.

Within eighteen months, the group reported dramatic, almost miraculous effects of prescribing the drug to intravenous heroin users. Their classic paper in the *Journal of the American Medical Association* is one of the most quoted in the medical literature, and with good reason. It still makes relevant and interesting reading today.

Dole's team found the transformation to be rapid and radical, with most of his patients returning to a normal way of life in all observable respects. Education was resumed, families reunited, employment found and, most importantly, the patients largely curtailed their use of injected heroin while taking daily doses of oral methadone.

In the thirty years since Dole's original study, many investigators around the world have confirmed his original findings[2]. It is believed that there were over 100,000 patients on methadone world-wide by the mid 1990s.

Back in 1980 however, some physicians were advocating low dose methadone and reduction doses over limited periods.

Though this ran contrary to Dole's original principles of management, it was attractive to those morally opposed to 'medical maintenance'. It also appealed to funding agencies as a way of saving money. By 1990 the HIV epidemic had taken its toll and research was clear that these therapeutic inadequacies had disastrous consequences. Such out-dated practices have now been largely abandoned[3].

Various refinements have been incorporated into modern practice to improve the outcomes and reduce unwanted effects. These aspects include longer periods in treatment, higher (or lower) doses as appropriate, the treatment of intercurrent illnesses and the use of intensive psychosocial supports[4]. Certain therapeutic situations require very close supervision while at other times patients are best left some freedom to direct their own rehabilitation. These are individual clinical decisions.

## WHAT HAPPENS WHEN COMMENCING METHADONE?

Methadone is a medical prescription. Before commencing it, the addict must have an assessment with a doctor. This includes a history, physical examination and a supervised urine test. Because methadone is a narcotic, the doctor must also obtain permission from the health authorities before prescribing. This can usually be done on the same day. Patients are then seen weekly at first, while stable patients are seen less often.

Many physical and mental changes happen when the drug user comes into methadone treatment. For the first time in what may be a very long time, the patient is free of cravings. Starting doses are usually 30-40mg. The period free of cravings may be brief at first, but as the medication builds up in the body this period should extend to twenty four hours. This may take up to three weeks and is sometimes called the 'honeymoon period'. After this, there should be no 'compulsive' drug seeking behaviour. A number of patients will still partake in narcotic use if others around them are doing so.

It is easy to recognise when the patient has reached their optimal dose. Their appetite returns, they sleep well and they begin to concentrate on other aspects of life such as family, work, education and (non-drug) recreation. Doses vary widely but most patients stabilise between 20mg and 120mg. The dose level is not related to the 'degree of addiction', but to the rate of metabolism. Thus there is no relation between the quantity of heroin consumed and subsequent dose of methadone needed. Urine test results reflect the patient's drug use and can usually detect narcotics for six days.

## 'PROBLEMS' WITH METHADONE

A number of patients gain weight when on methadone. This is caused by a combination of factors including increased food intake and less exercise. There is no evidence that methadone has a direct effect upon appetite or overall metabolism. On the other hand, the use of illicit heroin undoubtedly causes weight loss. Thus when on methadone, some patients simply return to their 'normal' body mass. A proportion of patients actually lose weight when on methadone treatment. This is also unexplained.

The only common side-effects of methadone treatment are constipation and sweating. Hence attention to hygiene, diet and exercise is important for these patients. In the drug using life style, many have forgotten or neglected dental hygiene and personal cleanliness. Gentle reminders from those who care may have the desired effect.

Recommendations about diet should be simple, practical and acceptable to the patients. Compulsive illicit drug users eat poorly, preferring fast foods, candy bars and soft drinks to more healthy staples[5]. All patients should be advised to eat two pieces of fruit per day. Those with bad constipation should also use a natural laxative such as prunes. Patients should be encouraged to drink sufficient water and to eat foods which are rich in fibre such as pineapple, sweet potato, carrots and bran-added breads.

They should be reminded that most cereals have low fibre ratings, and should be supplemented with unprocessed bran.

All adults need regular exercise, methadone patients being no exception. This aids digestion, blood pressure and the general level of fitness. Twice weekly formal exercise should be recommended at low levels for two hours or at higher levels for one hour. This can be as simple as a long walk or jog. Others will prefer cycling, tennis, swimming or going to the gym.

When used in the treatment of drug addiction, methadone is often given as a liquid. This is largely for historical and paternalistic reasons since tablets are known to work just as well. The syrup contains the active drug along with sugars and flavouring, with alcohol and benzoate as preservative. The liquid is unpopular with patients. 'Take-home' bottles may leak or break. The sugars may worsen dental problems. One practical benefit of a syrup is to enable small dose alterations.

A liquid presentation is also a temptation for those inclined to inject their take-away doses. The thick syrup was not designed for intravenous use and can cause severe pain when injected. Studies have shown that the majority of previous injectors who enter methadone treatment attempt to inject methadone at least once. In most cases this has no long term consequences.

A small minority continue to inject for longer periods, sometimes without apparent harm. Some such patients describe withdrawal symptoms coming on earlier due to increased metabolic clearance by the body following injection compared with the same dose given orally. This is a clinical problem which is addressed by various manoeuvres.

The granting of take-home doses is a vexed question in clinical practice. There is constant pressure to allow such doses to save patients time and money, but too many too early in rehabilitation lead to numerous problems which can rebound on the patient as well as the treatment generally. Most patients can safely be given single-day take home doses once per week.

## METHADONE: RESEARCH AND MYTHS

Both the safety and effectiveness of methadone treatment have been studied as closely as any medical topic. These investigations have revealed no permanent tissue damage from long term use of the drug. Apart from some minor constipation and sweating, there would appear to be no significant side-effects in the vast majority of those who take it[6].

Some members of self-help groups may utilise the drawbacks of methadone as a foundation to their individual decision to cease this and other forms of drug use. These sentiments may be appropriate in private motivational meetings, but they must never be used to persuade an individual against considering the treatment which can be life saving.

Drug dealers may have an interest in spreading stories about the supposed dangers of methadone. Misguided moral crusaders have also had a part to play in such myth-mongering. Addicts who join methadone treatment are a substantial loss to a lucrative black market. Rumours which have been spread include the 'rotting' of bones, teeth and bowels. Another story is that methadone is much more addicting than heroin and that nobody ever gets off it. Whether methadone is more or less addictive than heroin is like arguing whether spirits are more addictive than beer. It is interesting but unproductive speculation.

It is disappointing that the merits of methadone are still debated by those with no experience in the drug and alcohol field. Such ignorant people have succeeded in having methadone banned in certain areas such as Australia's Northern Territory and New Hampshire in the USA. This is to the great detriment of addicts and yields disastrous consequences for the wider community.

Large numbers of patients successfully complete methadone treatment every year. The average length of time in treatment is between one and two years. It is now known that compulsory reduction 'programs' have very low success rates and for this reason have been largely abandoned. A small proportion of patients seem to require methadone almost indefinitely.

Methadone should be seen as just one standard medical intervention for a complex behavioural problem. In many areas there are still restrictions upon doctors and patients which would be considered unacceptable in any other field[7]. These include limits to the numbers treated, artificial dosing regulations as well as the need for prior approval from health authorities before commencing treatment in each and every case.

When the epidemic of HIV/AIDS was recognised, some jurisdictions investigated methadone treatment, realising the likely benefits and relatively low cost. In some instances, it was introduced in some haste, with little preparation due to the urgency of the public health problem. Large clinics were established to expand the availability to large numbers of patients. The supply was often still inadequate for the demand, turning some clinics into focal points for drug dealing and crime as some patients were refused treatment. This was a source of spurious criticism for those opposed to methadone since such troubles were largely due to a lack of adequate treatment positions rather than the methadone itself.

It is interesting to hear some of those who are not in treatment talking of the difficulties of being on methadone; the 'inability to travel', 'high cost' and 'side effects'. Most patients who join methadone treatment talk about the opposite: the freedom it gives, the money it saves and the relief from unpleasant reactions from street drugs. For stable patients, methadone dosing locations can be altered by simply making a phone-call and sending a prescription by post or facsimile. If the patient is travelling beyond their own health jurisdiction, a letter to a physician in the new state or country is usually sufficient to continue the treatment elsewhere on a temporary basis.

The miracle of methadone has to be witnessed to be understood. The change in the addict is often sudden and dramatic. The appearance, attitude, general health and social functioning may return to normal almost overnight.

Following months or even years of illicit drug use, it is important to have a substantial period of stability on methadone before considering dose reductions. It has been shown repeatedly that those remaining in treatment longer have a better likelihood of long term abstinence from narcotics.

## PRESCRIBED HEROIN AND OTHER OPIOIDS

The prescription of heroin for addicts is nothing new. Doctors have been doing it all this century in Britain. There has been little good analysis and only one randomised trial which compared legal injected heroin with oral methadone[8]. This study showed comparable results in both groups after a year in treatment.

Another carefully controlled study was commenced in Switzerland in 1994. Injected heroin was prescribed to over a thousand heroin addicts in the clinic setting. All doses were for injection on the premises.

The candidates had to agree to initial randomisation into injected heroin, morphine or oral methadone groups. They then attended from one to three times daily for medication.

Preliminary results announced in 1996 were very positive. Patients' health, employment, legal and social parameters all improved. A number of patients also voluntarily transferred from intravenous heroin to oral methadone. Some patients were not able to tolerate morphine due to unpleasant side effects which did not occur on pure heroin.

A similar pilot trial has been proposed for Canberra, with subsequent involvement of other Australian cities. Although this has received an unprecedented level of community support, political and administrative obstacles have postponed it indefinitely.

The initial benefit from legal heroin is that more addicts may be attracted into treatment. It may also be appropriate for certain patients who have not done well on methadone and who drop out of treatment. The re-introduction of heroin as an analgesic would also be welcomed by many clinicians.   It is useful as a pre-operative medication as well as in palliative care.

Reports have been published of substantial numbers of patients being treated with alternative opioids such as buprenorphine, levomethadyl acetate ('LAAM' or long acting methadone) and dihydrocodeine.   There are also individual case reports of addicts being stabilised on shorter acting opioids such as dextromoramide and morphine.

⌘

# 5

## "GETTING OFF METHADONE"

**WHEN TO BEGIN REDUCTIONS**
**'CO-DEPENDENCY'**
**HOW TO REDUCE DOSES**
**"PLAN B"**

**WHEN TO BEGIN REDUCTIONS**

The incentive to come off methadone treatment may come from many quarters. One common reason is the rigour of the treatment itself. Dispensary hours may be very limited, such as from 9 to 11am. Patients may have to attend every day, even on weekends when transport is difficult. The methadone dose levels may be inadequate and 'penalties' may be incurred when days are missed. Some clinics may deny patients medication if they are unable to pass a urine specimen on the spot.

These difficulties can result in frustration and rejection of the treatment by the patient. It is important to realise that patients who withdraw from methadone for these reasons alone have a very high relapse rate, perhaps as high as 90%. In other cases, there may be other more valid reasons behind the initial catalyst. Such factors may include an intention to have a baby, a strong desire for abstinence or a need to travel to areas where methadone is not available.

Another consideration sometimes given for withdrawal from methadone is religious. This rationale treats methadone as 'just another mind altering drug' rather than as a prescribed medicine.  Drugs and alcohol are an entrenched part of many organised religions.  Devout Jews and Christians celebrate the Sabbath by drinking wine.  There was alcohol at 'the last supper' and one of the miracles Jesus is said to have performed was the converting of water into wine, further sanctifying the beverage. Other religious groups use cannabis, peyote cactus or other drugs for ceremonial or spiritual purposes.  Hence a religious edict against drug or alcohol use is upheld by some but completely contrary to other religious observances.  In either case, it should not influence the correct treatment of an unstable drug user in the short term.

## 'CO-DEPENDENCY'

This is a term which means different things to different people.  Some psychologists and counsellors use the term to refer to other active parties in a drug user's sphere.  This should not be confused with dual dependency which is when a person is addicted to two drugs simultaneously, especially alcohol, tranquillizers or narcotics.  In some cases one drug is used to excess because of the lack of the 'primary' drug of addiction. The 'secondary' drug may also be more harmful, and the person therefore at greater risk.  This may occur in patients on inadequate doses of methadone and who are still abusing other drugs, including non-opiates.  On the other hand, 'co-dependency' is an interesting concept but a difficult and ill-defined term.  It might be best avoided except by professionals.

## HOW TO REDUCE DOSES

Given that the patient has been stable on a regular methadone dose for at least four weeks and is suitably motivated, then a reduction of approximately 10% of the daily dose may be undertaken as a trial.  This should always be organised a few days ahead, as it is never an urgent decision.  This allows a change of mind and delayed reductions if the patient lacks confidence.  Pressure from others to reduce doses is destabilising and must be resisted.

As long as the patient tolerates the new dose, then a further 10% reduction may be taken after a further two weeks. The steady state blood level of methadone is not achieved until five to seven days after a dose change, so it is inappropriate to alter doses within the one week. A two week period therefore allows this second week to see if the lower level is tolerated.

A simplistic theory stated by many people goes: 'if you reduce the dose steadily over a certain period, the addict should be able to cut the medicine out altogether and their addiction will be conquered'. Even a number of addicts hold to this attractive but erroneous belief. It has been tried a thousand times! If it were true, then addicts would all be able to cure themselves, and there would be no problem, and no books like this! It simply does not work, and denies the very nature of compulsive behaviour. It would be as useful as saying to an overweight person to 'if you eat a bit less every day you will cure your obesity'. Of course, it *is* true, but to recite it is patronising, unhelpful and shows an ignorance of the human condition.

But gradual reductions *do* work in certain instances. Usually over quite extended periods, they should be initiated by the patient themselves in a climate of stability and control. Generally the dose reduction increments are 10mg above 80mg and 5mg steps at lower levels. Some patients request 2½mg increments below 20mg. Everyone agrees that the most difficult period of reductions is the last 20mg. This may take even longer than the time taken to reduce from 80mg to 20mg. And we now know that the longer it takes, the more likely it is to result in long term abstinence.

The temptation to use other medications during methadone reductions may be strong. Sleep is often a problem, but tranquillizers and sedatives are not appropriate. Headaches and other pain syndromes may occur. Aspirin or paracetamol (US: acetominophen) may help temporary pains, but it is illogical to use the stronger narcotic pain killers. Codeine in small doses such as 8mg will have little effect, while larger doses will give a greater narcotic 'habit', placing abstinence at an even greater distance. Such drugs will also confuse the interpretation of urine testing if this is part of the patient's treatment regimen.

There are other ways of relieving these problems without resorting to drugs. Massage, exercise, herbal remedies, vitamins and diet can all be of benefit in some cases. Alternative therapies such as acupuncture and hypnosis may also have a role in some patients.

The 'last dose' may be a planned affair, but more often the patient on quite low doses, such as 2.5-10mg, will just decide to cease attending the dispensary.

There have been reports of addicted patients who were given a narcotic antagonist such as naloxone or naltrexone experimentally while under a prolonged anaesthetic. This is an extreme measure to consider, and shows the length to which some people will go to overcome their addiction. How long the abstinence lasts and what incidence of ill-effects ensues may be determined by future formal studies.

**PLAN "B"**

If the patient becomes too ill during reductions or after the last dose, then it may become necessary to review the prescription. The symptoms of such 'illness' can mimic many other medical conditions. If illicit heroin is used on more than one occasion then it is nearly always necessary to reinstitute full methadone maintenance treatment.

Such a course should not be seen as admitting defeat or failure. It is merely a demonstration that the addict's body is still conditioned to narcotics and is not yet ready for abstinence. This very exercise may be important for some addicts and their doctors in justifying continued long-term treatment. Where the person is stable and in control, it may be possible to keep the dose in the low range, but where there are signs of instability or medical illness, the dose usually needs to be restored to the previous maintenance levels.

⌘

# 6

---

# "THE LONG HAUL"

---

**THE NATURAL HISTORY OF DRUG ADDICTION**
**FAMOUS DRUG USERS**
**RESEARCH**
**MORTALITY IN DRUG USERS**
**PAINFUL DISORDERS**
**PSYCHIATRIC CONDITIONS**
**OTHER MEDICAL CONDITIONS**

**THE NATURAL HISTORY OF DRUG ADDICTION**

An old aphorism called the *'ten year rule'* holds that most addicts consume drugs for a period of ten years before giving up. While not hard and fast, it seems to apply as much to smokers, compulsive drinkers and heroin addicts. Some have died before the ten year mark, but those who make it may have a bright future if they play their cards wisely.

When done at the right time, withdrawal from drugs can be relatively painless and quite rewarding. For the addict, detoxification is a positive and active process. The timing and motivation are both important to success. It is during this time that dependence upon the drug must be replaced by other positive things in daily life.

Another old saying goes: *'Once an addict, always an addict'.* This is often stated by drug users themselves, and it may be more relevant than it sounds. Like 'recovering' or 'ex'-alcoholics, many dry alcoholics still state that they are *alcoholic* until the day they die. It is true that heroin addicts who have not used the drug for a number of years are still at risk of returning to drug use should certain circumstances arise. This may mean easy availability of the drug or painful life situations, or both.

Throughout history there have been waves of drug and alcohol use. When new drugs are introduced into naïve populations, there is a sudden rush of enthusiasm, followed by a learning process as the drug is assimilated by the community. Substances with the greatest market penetration are the stimulants caffeine and nicotine, contained in coffee, tea and tobacco.

Opium was so popular in China in the nineteenth century that in some provinces over 80% of adult males were addicted. In Victorian England there were enormous amounts of narcotic consumed, amounting to tons of Turkish opium imported each year. Australia has also had an enormous appetite for narcotics in the forms of mixed analgesics.

It is said that alcoholic spirits were first used by large numbers of Americans during the prohibition period. Previously popular only with the rich, spirits were the best way for individuals to smuggle enough alcohol for a party. And the party continues today, for better or for worse!

**FAMOUS DRUG USERS**
**Thomas De Quincey** (b.1785) was the first to describe his own addiction in detail. In his 1821 classic, *Confessions of an English Opium Eater*, he broaches most of the issues faced by addicts today. Even the title was shocking to readers of the time, as it was believed that only Asians could become addicted to opium. Reworked and expanded by the author in 1856, the book's wordy style is a little heavy for the modern reader but De Quincey's detailed self-analysis is absolutely fresh and relevant to the human condition of all ages. He covers the intense feeling of well-being imparted by the drug as well as the ambivalence often experienced by opium users.

He contrasts the relatively minor adverse consequences of opium with the destructive effects of alcohol. In his introduction he also describes the rabble encountered in a rural apothecary at opening time and the seemingly enormous doses of opium dispensed to the addicts. The urgency with which the customers, mostly agricultural workers, jostled for service is typical of what happens in some methadone dispensaries today.

First prescribed opium for a dyspeptic condition, De Quincey lived a long and productive life, dying in his seventies after more than forty years of drug use. He was just one of many prominent people who we know were addicted to opioids.

There was a group of nineteenth century poets and philosophers whose members took to opium. Some were known to be addicted, others partaking on a more casual basis. While some facts are known, other details remain speculative.

**Dr William Stewart Halsted** (1852 - 1922) is known as the father of American surgery. He pioneered the cancer saving operation, the mastectomy, at a time when cure from the disease was unknown. He popularised the use of rubber gloves in the operating theatres and introduced several other important advances in surgical technique including improved blood transfusion. He used daily morphine for most of his long life.

Other famous people who took opium included Roman Emperor Marcus Aurelius who suffered with joint pains, William Wilberforce (1759 - 1833), Samuel Taylor Coleridge, Timothy Leary (d.1996), William Burroughs (b. 1916) to name but a few.

Numerous practising doctors, lawyers, politicians and business people use heroin and some have become addicted. A proportion of these are nowadays on methadone treatment, mostly unbeknownst to their colleagues and clients.

What is important from our standpoint is that such people are productive members of society at the same time as using large quantities of opioid drugs. Most of them only use drugs for limited periods but some consume their drugs regularly over many years.

**RESEARCH**

Twin studies show a higher rate of addiction in identical than fraternal siblings, proving a genetic component to this behaviour. The high concordance in siblings generally is partly genetic and partly environmental. Adopted children brought up by alcoholic parents may also grow up with alcohol problems, indicating an environmental component.

A previous attempt to find a gene for alcoholism found a preponderance of some particular sequences, but failed to account for the narrow ethnicity of the subjects. When fully examined, this invalidated the would-be exciting results. Future work in this area will have to be more rigorous by utilising a broad cross-section of ethnic groups and strict scientific methods.

Much new work is being done in the field of DNA typing. It is highly likely that there are multiple genetic factors in the development of drug addiction, including personality, behavioural, metabolic and other effects. When these are added to environmental factors, the causes for drug addiction may be better elucidated.

Studies in Britain prior to the HIV epidemic showed that after seven years, about a third of narcotic users have ceased all drugs, 10% are dead, 10% are in jail and approximately 40% are still in receipt of a legal prescription, mostly methadone[9]. Comparable results have been found in Australia more recently. In the United States, the nature of the society and limited availability of treatment make comparisons more difficult.

**MORTALITY IN DRUG USERS**

Lives are lost frequently in the drug using population, and very often it is not the victim's drug-of-choice which kills them. Substitute drugs, harmful additives and unknown concentrations or alternative routes of administration are all possible causes of death. Even with tobacco, few, if any die from nicotine poisoning, but nearly 20,000 Australians perish every year from the consequences of smoking.

Studies of untreated narcotic users show an annual mortality between 1.5% and 7%[2,7]. A proportion of patients have hepatitis and HIV contracted before treatment commenced. One study found that patients on methadone maintenance had mortality rates close to that of the non-drug using population[10].

In a large Scandinavian study, it was found that death rates in street heroin addicts were 63 times greater than for matched subjects who did not use illicit drugs[11]. They also demonstrated an eight-fold reduction in deaths of those going into methadone treatment. Those leaving treatment voluntarily had death rates of half that again. Some patients who were discharged from treatment due to various 'infringements' had mortality rates which returned to 55 times those predicted for non drug users. We now know that these were the very patients most in need of treatment services, being at highest risk of death and other complications. Involuntary discharge should no longer occur in ethical treatment services.

Although it was probably sub-optimal by today's standards, the methadone treatment given to the Scandinavian subjects was still dramatically effective in preventing deaths due to all causes.

In a study of all 152 New South Wales heroin related deaths reported in 1992, researchers found that only 2% of these occurred in patients currently enrolled in methadone treatment[12]. Another 26% of the victims were previously registered for methadone treatment, which was relatively freely available at that time. Thus over two thirds of such deaths occurred in those who had never been registered for methadone treatment. A number of these may have been on waiting lists, some may have lived in areas without treatment services while some occasional users may not have qualified for treatment.

These high mortality rates are thus very largely preventable by the use of methadone where appropriate. Each death represents an enormous cost to the community, not to mention the dozens of non-fatal overdoses which occur for each fatal one. Methadone is a relatively cheap and simple medical treatment, costing as little as $7 per day and utilising services already available in the community.

In Amsterdam, (pop. 700,000) it was estimated that 80% of 7,000 regular heroin users were in touch with treatment services. Of these, approximately 3,500 were on methadone at any one time in 1995[13]. The total annual drug-related mortality (direct and indirect) in both 1992 and 1993 was 1.9% of the estimated drug using population.

A number of heroin overdoses apparently occur in patients who have recently left treatment. Another common overdose scenario is in those recently released from prison. They may have little or no tolerance and the street drugs may be of unaccustomed strength. In some jails there is now a move to permit prisoners to commence or recommence methadone treatment before release. Other prison systems still do not permit methadone treatment despite the evidence of its practical benefits to those incarcerated and to society generally. The denial of methadone in this way may breach international treaty obligations and it effectively punishes addicted offenders twice for their crimes.

Sporadic deaths of patients have been reported in the stabilisation period of methadone treatment. These may be minimised by graduated dose increases and regular clinical assessments.

The finding of an eight-fold drop in the death rate of heroin addicts entering methadone treatment translates to a massive saving of lives. More than a quarter of victims in the New South Wales heroin overdose study had previously been on methadone treatment, but were not afforded its protection at the time of death.

It can be conservatively extrapolated from the studies that of the 17,000 patients on methadone Australia-wide in 1996, in excess of 250 lives are saved annually. This is in addition to the other substantial benefits already seen in areas of employment, reduced criminality and the prevention of viral disease transmission. At a modest cost to the community methadone treatment easily pays for itself in all these ways.

Only a minority of these patients fit the 'junkie' stereotype and some are very young, emphasising the tragedy of these largely preventable deaths. Such observations further justify the continued expansion of ethical prescribing of methadone by doctors in the treatment and control of heroin addiction.

## PAINFUL DISORDERS

A number of addicts date their first drug use to pain killers prescribed by doctors for common conditions like back pain, migraine or shingles. Injected narcotics are also commonly used after motor accidents involving fractures and soft tissue injuries. Subsequent scarring can also lead to chronic pain syndromes which may sometimes require narcotic pain killers.

For those who are already using heroin or other narcotics, opioids will only relieve pain if prescribed in substantially higher doses than the regular daily intake. Drug withdrawals will invariably worsen such pains.

Where possible, corrective treatments are preferable to the use of pain killers. These include physiotherapy, arthritis medication or surgery. Alternative treatments such as acupuncture and manipulative manoeuvres may also help a proportion of cases.

When all such attempts fail to control symptoms narcotic analgesics may be required. Many non-addicted patients show no signs of addiction and can use the drugs when needed depending on the degree of pain. Others develop the addiction syndrome. Patients who lose control of their analgesic drug use often respond well to treatment given in much the same manner as when used for illicit drug use.

Methadone is now a popular modality with pain specialists due to its long half-life, oral absorption, safety and economy. Patients also find it very acceptable as a simple alternative to what may have previously been complex combined therapy.

It is a great pity that a number of doctors are still reluctant to prescribe strong pain killers to addicts who are suffering from painful medical conditions. These patients deserve pain relief just as much as other medical patients, and since they have an established tolerance to narcotics they may require higher doses for the same analgesic effect. The main factor against the more liberal use of opiates, the risk of addiction, is academic in these patients.

## PSYCHIATRIC CONDITIONS

Numerous heroin addicts suffer from depressive, anxiety, and psychotic disorders. Some may pre-date the substance abuse, others accompany it and in others still, the psychiatric illness comes on after the addiction is well established.

Schizophrenic symptoms may be helped, at least temporarily, by opioids. Like other unpleasant sensations, delusions may be quelled and a sense of relaxation induced. It is said that prior to the introduction of major tranquillizers in the 1950s, opioids were occasionally used in treating these disorders. It is thus not surprising that some schizophrenic patients who are introduced to heroin develop a habit on the drug. These patients are less organised and may be more prone to complications of intravenous drug use. Such patients, however, only rarely have the resources to obtain large quantities of illicit drugs and they may also be more readily able to cease such drug use than other addicts.

People who abuse alcohol or tranquillizers often become depressed. This depression responds best to withdrawal of the agent causing the symptoms. Those who develop a true 'endogenous' depression whilst using other drugs may go un-recognised for a time. Opioids such as heroin and methadone are not anti-depressants. Depressed patients respond well to normal medical interventions, and should never be denied treatment just because they are 'recovering addicts'. The principles of

*Alcoholics* and *Narcotics Anonymous* uphold the right of the addict to receive all normal medical treatment, as long as this does not entail the consumption of alcohol or narcotics.

Those with such true depressive illness usually respond well to anti-depressant drugs such as tricyclics (eg Sinequan, Prothiaden), tetracyclics (eg Tolvon), MAO inhibitors or the newer agents, serotonin-specific re-uptake inhibitors (SSRI's eg. Prozac, Aropax, Zoloft). Those with 'situational' or 'exogenous' depression should receive counselling, psychosocial support and careful adjustment of their methadone doses.

## OTHER MEDICAL CONDITIONS

The incidence of hepatitis C infection amongst injecting drug users is over 90% in some studies. No immunisation currently exists. Only a minority of patients develop symptoms of fever and yellow jaundice. This means that most cases were unrecognised or 'sub-clinical' hepatitis C infections.

The long-term natural history of this illness is still unclear since it has only been tested for since 1990. Some alarmist media reports have played on this uncertainty, causing unnecessary anguish in patients and their families. What *is* clear is that over half of these cases get over the infection rapidly with no sign of on-going liver damage. A proportion, however, have continuing liver inflammation which shows up in blood tests. This 'chronic persistent hepatitis' is often of no consequence short term. An unknown number of these patients will develop cirrhosis or liver cancer up to 20 years later.

The means of transmission of hepatitis C usually involves blood or blood products. However, there are a number of reports of transmission in patients who seem not to have shared syringes or have other risk factors. These people have nearly always used drugs in the presence of others and it is possible that the means of spread involves the skin, droplets, spoon, tourniquet or even the drug itself. Current treatment is only marginally effective at suppressing disease activity.

Hepatitis B can also cause a chronic active or persistent hepatitis in drug users. It is found in about a third of those who injected heroin in Australia in the 1980s. Like hepatitis C, it is often a sub-clinical illness, but it can also occur as a serious, acute infection with profound fatigue, jaundice, weight loss and fever. This can also lead to cirrhosis, chronic liver failure and, in rare cases, cancer. Although liver failure can now be treated successfully with organ transplantation, the rare liver cancer called hepatoma is usually fatal. Immunisation is protective.

The human immunodeficiency virus (HIV) has not spread in the Australian drug using population as it has elsewhere. In some parts of Europe and America the incidence is between 30% and 50% amongst injectors. In Australia this figure has remained below 2%, despite HIV spreading to Australia very early in the epidemic. This was due to a co-ordinated strategy including the availability of syringes, methadone treatment and an education campaign.

Methadone is relatively safe during pregnancy. While it is desirable for all pregnant women to be drug free, the risks of heroin use are very high, and easily outweigh any theoretical drawbacks of methadone. In heroin users, miscarriage, still-birth, pre-term delivery and failure to thrive occur with greater frequency. This is in addition to the risks of overdose, viral infections, thrombosis and social consequences. Studies have shown that the majority of babies born to women on methadone are healthy. Outcomes are greatly improved when compared with women who are still using illicit drugs.

Babies may have a temporary narcotic requirement needing reducing doses of morphine for withdrawal effects. Breast feeding is now encouraged by most specialists, even for mothers on higher doses of methadone. The long term effects of such exposure in early life is unlikely to be significant while the benefits of breast milk are substantial.

⌘

# 7

# SELECTED CASE HISTORIES

To demonstrate the diversity of heroin addiction, the following is a group of sample stories based on personal events related by patients presenting for treatment at a doctor's surgery.  These vignettes are necessarily brief windows into the lives of drug users.  By their nature, they only include those whose drug use has become unmanageable.

### COMMON PRESENTATION FOR TREATMENT
Victor, an asthmatic aged 25, is asking for help.  Having begun with alcohol and cannabis as a very young teenager, he first used heroin at the age of 16 with his elder brother.  He never had a regular job and spent four episodes in boys' homes and jail for burglaries and shop stealing offences.  He is currently using half a 'weight' of heroin daily, worth approximately $200, in two to three injections.  He had 'hepatitis', but never returned to find out which type.

He is requesting methadone treatment in order to kick his heroin habit.  The police have given him 'one last warning' to stop his small time dealing which he does to finance his drug use.  His girlfriend is pregnant and he says that he wants to 'settle down and get a job'.

This man is prescribed methadone by his GP, with dispensing from his local pharmacy on a daily basis.  Over a couple of weeks, he receives 40mg, then 50mg and after that, 60mg daily.  Once on 60mg, he ceases the use of illicit drugs and he also decides to give up cigarettes.  He is accepted into a computer training course. Victor wishes to reduce his dose to 40mg immediately, but is persuaded to continue the higher dose until after the computer course is over when he may be in a better position to address his dependence issues.

## COMPLICATIONS, THEN ABSTINENCE

Nicholas was a nice child who was always polite and agreeable. He was shy with other people and not comfortable in crowds. Alcohol made him more 'confident' and by the age of 20 he was drinking heavily. He was offered some heroin at a party in which the same needle was shared. The drug made him feel bold and assertive for the first time and he began to use it every day. He ceased drinking at this period also.

Six weeks later he developed fever, vomiting and jaundice. He was diagnosed with hepatitis B, probably from the dirty needle at the party. After the worst of the illness, he was admitted to the local hospital where he was transferred to the 'detox' ward. Here he learned about addiction as a disease, *Twelve Step* programs and *Narcotics Anonymous*. He felt a great rapport with others in the group and after four days drying out, determined never to use heroin or alcohol again.

It took him two months to get over the fatigue brought on by the hepatitis. He used the time to become active in the *N.A.* movement. Nicholas attended meetings every day at first, reciting his sad story of alcohol and then heroin abuse. He developed a confident manner in public speaking, quite reversing his former shyness. He then decided to pursue a career in radio, feeling that this would be an opportunity to spread the good news and help others.

## DEATH IN A PRISON CELL

Michelle went to an exclusive ladies college and was first introduced to drugs at university. She dropped out in the first year after first using cannabis and then smoking opium. She lived with her six-month-old baby and her boyfriend who was injecting heroin.

Her family disowned her but she secretly kept in touch with her alcoholic aunt who helped with the baby. Michelle spent some time in Asia and did some 'trips' importing drugs. On one such, she was caught by customs and committed to prison on remand. Since she was in severe heroin withdrawals the prison medical staff recommended methadone treatment. She refused the offer as she had been told that methadone was more addictive than heroin and that it blocked out the 'rush' from heroin.

A week later, Michelle was found dead in her cell from a heroin overdose.

Although previously a heavy heroin user, her tolerance may have abated after a week without the drug. In the prison system as on the streets, there is often little time to gauge the strength of a drug owing to risk of being caught and the nature of contraband substances.

## TEN YEARS ON METHADONE

Peter went to the local selective high school where he was first introduced to injected heroin. He started a successful computer business, using heroin intermittently for five years before moving to Hong Kong for a year. While away, he used no opioids, but drank a lot of duty-free alcohol and smoked cannabis occasionally.

On his return to Australia he rapidly developed a heroin habit, spending over $200 in three daily injections. He borrowed from his father who was a dentist. He was also caught growing his own cannabis plants and court proceedings were under way when he presented at the local community care centre for assessment.

He was prescribed oral methadone syrup which enabled him to cease heroin altogether. He resumed his computer work and paid off his debts.

After six months he was given weekend take-away doses by the clinic. He often took both doses together on the Saturday, leaving him short and a bit jaded by the Monday morning. He did this for three years without apparent problems. Tuesday and Thursday take home doses also caused problems. His work colleagues found that on Mondays and Wednesdays he was vague and sleepy with small pupils.

He asked his clinic to give him daily doses, but was not frank about the reasons. They could not understand his request, as he was their 'best' patient ... he had a regular job, he was married and his (non-drug using) wife recently had a baby. He never put in a 'dirty' urine test (only abusing methadone) and he seemed to have everything going for him.

One Easter holiday revealed what was happening. He had used up all his doses by Easter Saturday, having taken two extra on the Thursday night and the rest on Good Friday. By the Monday night, he was in a panic with severe withdrawals coming on. His wife called the emergency doctor who diagnosed kidney stones and gave an injection of morphine.

He now became frank with his wife and his new methadone prescriber about his 'double dosing'. X-rays demonstrated no kidney stones, so his backache was put down to withdrawals. Peter stated that he just could not help himself when he had extra doses available, and just swallowed them. His doctor ordered a methadone level which showed a low level. Thus his dose was increased slightly and his wife offered to supervise the weekend doses.

Peter continued on with these arrangements for a further six years. His business prospered, his daughter is growing up and he feels that he is a full member of society. Further business trips to Asia have been accomplished by utilising the availability of methadone in Hong Kong. He was also permitted to take extra doses on brief stop-overs in places such as Singapore, Seoul and Bangkok where methadone was not so readily available.

### TWIN SISTERS WITH DRUGS IN THE BLOOD

Twin sisters Stella and Stareen were born to one of the city's best known drug dealers. Mrs Smith had a council house near the airport.  From here, she arranged Asian drug trips, couriers, false passports and visas as well as an efficient local distribution network.  She also unwittingly developed a habit of her own by first sniffing and then smoking the heroin which she had been dealing with.

The twins were growing up with drugs all around them. Their early years were punctuated by clients coming and going, police raids, people shooting up out the back and other drug world goings on.  It still came as a shock for Mrs Smith to learn that her twins, now aged 15, were using heroin taken from her 'stash'.

In spite of seeing all the problems of drug use, they had sniffed it the first couple of times and then found a way of injecting each other with the drug.

This all came to light when Mrs Smith was raided for the last time and caught with a large quantity of heroin.  She was charged with drug dealing and sentenced to ten years jail.  The twins were placed in the care of a country rehabilitation service, near to the mother's prison farm.

In jail, Mrs Smith became a born-again Christian.  She started a prison drug support group and renounced her life of crime.

## MIDDLE CLASS ADDICT

James is a 32 year old council engineer.  He was referred to the drug and alcohol centre because his girlfriend of six years broke off the relationship when she discovered he was using heroin.  He had used cannabis since his teens, and at age 30 began using oral amphetamine.  He stated that it helped with his second job as a session guitarist.  His dealer had run out of 'speed' and suggested he try heroin, saying that 'you cannot get addicted if you don't use the needle'.  After trying the heroin nasally he gave up all the other drugs.  He 'snorted' heroin on a daily basis for twelve months prior to presenting for treatment.

James had lost interest in food, work and sex.  He was sleeping poorly and he was under-weight.  He had infected gums and several dental cavities. He had an episode of double vision which prevented him from driving and he had used up all his sick pay. He was negative for HIV and hepatitis B and C. He had tried to cease using heroin on several occasions, both at home and in a detox centre.

He opted for methadone treatment and after six weeks had used no heroin and was talking to his fiancée again. He had no more time off work. While on 25mg of methadone daily he paid off some debts, attended the dentist, got back into training and put on some weight. Once stable on methadone maintenance treatment, he was better able to decide when and how he wishes to deal with his dependency.

## DISASTER TO DOMESTICITY

Cheryl had been a street working prostitute for ten years. She used $800 worth of heroin in five to six injections daily. She also took up to 60mg of temazepam for sleeping and was a regular cocaine user. The clinic told her that her hepatitis C infection was 'active' and treatment was needed. Though having epilepsy as a child, there were no recent fits. She was wanted by the police for unpaid fines.

Her two children's foster parents were killed in a car accident and she determined to get her life into order to care for them again. Methadone treatment was commenced through her GP who was a licensed prescriber. A conciliation visit to the chamber magistrate permitted an extension on her outstanding fines. Public housing was then arranged on an urgent basis due to the plight of the children. At the patient's request, she was also placed on a reducing scale of diazepam (Valium) which was dispensed at the same time as her methadone.

In this time she ceased all illicit drug use. Liver tests showed significant improvements and specialist opinion advised continued observation. She was reunited with her children after satisfying the family court officials of her home situation.

## METHADONE "JUST IN CASE"

Fritz had been out of jail for three months this time. He was diagnosed HIV positive three years earlier after a bout of shingles. His doctor said that his immune function was good with T cells greater than 250.

Now living in the country with his sister, Fritz had used no heroin since coming out of jail. On many occasions over the years he had been apprehended with heroin in his possession, or committing crimes to support his habit. He was on a good behaviour bond which would see him jailed again if he had any further convictions. During previous episodes on methadone he had used little heroin, but he had returned to heroin use after dose reductions. Although he did not have a current habit, he requested methadone again since he was moving back to the city.

He commenced oral methadone at 15mg daily which was gradually increased to 35mg over two weeks. After six weeks, he got a job in the city and kept out of trouble. His immune function remained good and he did a course in HIV education and counselling.

## SABOTAGE FROM WITHIN

Sarah, a university graduate, ceased using heroin on low-dose methadone. She was looking after her six year old son and doing some part-time work at her old school. Several attempts at methadone dose reductions had led to relapses to heroin use. She was never happy on methadone treatment and eventually joined a Christian fellowship with whose help she managed to kick drugs, including the 'methadone habit'.

She subsequently become a veritable nuisance to her old clinic. In her belief that methadone was bad for patients, Sarah began hanging around the office. With her new-found evangelism, she tried to 'convert' methadone patients to a life of abstinence with Jesus.

The difficulties and doubts harboured by those with chemical dependency make this sort of talk very unsettling. They were being told that there is an 'easier, more virtuous way' to give up drugs, by using 'faith, hope and charity'.

After being banned from the clinic, Sarah began a 'methadone support group'. By past performance, this may turn out to be another thinly disguised 'methadone hate group', serving no useful purpose except to appease Sarah's insecurities.

**THIS TIME, FOR SURE!**

Michael's family no longer spoke to him as he had persistently stolen items from the house, including his mother's jewellery.

He attended the methadone clinic again after an absence of some months. He said that he really wanted to kick the habit this time. He had worked up a number of drug debts since getting out of prison. Reminded of his previous poor performance and three 'false starts' on methadone, he was permitted another trial of treatment.

Attending for his second dose the following morning, he was chased by a man with an iron bar. The attacker bid a retreat when he realised he was in a drug referral clinic.

However, he apparently later caught up with Michael, who arrived two days later with several broken ribs and a black eye. Michael carried his worldly effects with some difficulty and said that he was leaving town for good. He had one last dose and was not seen again.

⌘

# APPENDIX

**OTHER DRUGS: NICOTINE/TOBACCO**
          **CANNABIS**
          **ALCOHOL**
          **AMPHETAMINE AND ECSTASY**
          **LSD, MAGIC MUSHROOMS, PEYOTE**
          **COCAINE**

**OTHER DRUGS: NICOTINE/TOBACCO**
     Nicotine is one of the most addictive substances known. It can be consumed in the form of smoked tobacco, mouth wads or as snuff. Remarkably, it took over three hundred years for western doctors to recognise the disastrous health consequences of smoking. It is by far the most harmful drug, with almost 20,000 Australians dying annually as a result in the 1990s. It has been shown that over 50% of smokers will die prematurely as a direct result of tobacco induced illnesses.

     Now that the duplicity of the tobacco companies has been exposed, a more logical approach is being taken by most western governments in protecting consumers and minimising the risks to smokers. This includes a choice of quality product availability, tax based on drug content, filters, truthful labelling, a ban on advertising, education campaigns and subsidised treatment for those needing it.

     The principle of nicotine patch and gum treatment for smokers has close parallels with the use of replacement methadone for heroin addicts. The addictive component, nicotine, is given in a long acting and relatively harmless form, thus avoiding the injurious constituents of tobacco smoke such as carbon monoxide, tar, soot and other burnt by-products.

Nicotine patches have been widely studied in recent years including 'double blind' trials. There is no doubt that they are very safe and effective treatments for smokers. Their use at least doubles the number of quitters who remain abstinent from tobacco at six to twelve months. Many of the ex-smokers have also ceased the patches by this time.

About 90% of heroin addicts also smoke cigarettes. When in treatment, a proportion give up each year, some with the aid of patches or nicotine chewing gum, others by just going 'cold turkey'.

## OTHER DRUGS: CANNABIS

Cannabis is a widely used drug with a relatively low potential for harm when compared with heroin, alcohol and tobacco. It is technically illegal throughout the world, but is tolerated in some jurisdictions such as Holland, Alaska, South Australia, Northern Territory and the Australian Capital Territory. It is usually smoked as dried leaf and flowering heads. It can also be used in the concentrated form called hashish. This can be smoked or incorporated into food such as biscuits or cake. It is a tar-like substance which can be broken up into a cigarette or 'bong'.

Cannabinol drugs are not addictive in the ordinary sense, but they can occasionally be associated with a psychological dependence. In such cases, the patient may spend inordinate amounts of time and money consuming the drug. Many such patients are gainfully employed although their finances and recreation time may be in disarray.

This drug was banned in the 1930s in America for reasons which are now known to have been related to commerce in hemp substitutes for the manufacture of paper. There was opposition to the bans by the medical profession. Indeed, many pharmaceutical preparations contained extract of cannabis as a major active ingredient. This was one of the few available drugs which had demonstrated beneficial actions with minimal side effects. It was useful in treating nausea, vomiting, anorexia, sleep disturbances and anxiety.

Cannabis use is not harmless. Like other burnt inhalations, it contains carcinogens, tar and carbon monoxide. Hence it causes respiratory inflammation and the risk of cancer. It has been estimated that these effects are more dangerous than tobacco smoke, but because a smaller quantity of cannabis is smoked on average, the degree of damage is probably less than that from tobacco.

There has been much publicity concerning the risk of cannabis causing motor accidents. This appears to have been based on anecdotal cases and personal concerns rather than scientific evidence. Most studies in this area point towards alcohol as being the major substance implicated in road accidents. There is even an indication that those who use cannabis drink less alcohol and therefore may be at *reduced* risk on the roads. This has yet to be examined definitively.

## OTHER DRUGS: ALCOHOL

The 'demon drink' is also a major problem in those with other addictions. Many heroin addicts do not drink at all. Some others only have drinking problems when they are off the heroin, while a small number drink excessively regardless of their intake of other drugs.

Breath tests can be used in the clinical setting to underline the obvious. Results should not, however be used in any way other than in the patient's interest. There are also blood tests ($\gamma$GT and 'carbohydrate reduced transferrin') which give an accurate indication of the average alcohol consumption over previous weeks or months.

Alcohol is the commonest drug involved in overdose deaths. It causes depressed breathing which is worsened by narcotics and tranquillizers. It is not widely known that adults can also die from acute alcohol intoxication alone. This may result from the ingestion of large amounts of spirits in "I dare you" situations.

The commonest problems with alcohol, however, are behavioural. Family violence, drownings, motor accidents and crowd brawls are all closely associated with drinking. Medical consequences include acid dyspepsia, stomach ulcers, hepatitis, liver failure, heart disease, neuritis, brain damage, and dementia.

## OTHER DRUGS: BENZODIAZEPINE TRANQUILLIZERS

These drugs were introduced as the successors to the barbiturates in the early 1960s. After thirty years of experience, they have been found to have many complications of their own including an addictive potential, respiratory depression, fits, amnesia and balance problems in the elderly. They are not ideal drugs for chronic anxiety and insomnia for which they were previously recommended.

The abuse potential is substantial and the only treatment is graduated reductions. Self help groups are also of assistance for some.

## OTHER DRUGS: AMPHETAMINE AND ECSTASY

Amphetamine, metamphetamine (speed), dex-amphetamine and methylphenydate (Ritalin) are all addictive stimulants. They prevent sleep and keep subjects active for hours or even days. At the end of the period of drug use, the subject becomes exhausted and depressed with extended periods of sleep.

Many truck drivers, motor cycle enthusiasts and rock band players use these drugs, some for extended periods without apparent problems. A number, however, come to the attention of the authorities due to serious complications such as road accidents, overdoses and addiction.

These drugs are used in the treatment of narcolepsy, a rare sleeping disorder. They have also been recommended as long-term treatment for children with attention deficit disorder and some cases of brain damage. Advocated by a number of paediatricians, this form of prescribing is difficult to study objectively. The management of these children as they reach adult life addicted to stimulants is also uncharted medical terrain.

Although no doctor would advocate recreational stimulants, the adage that 'speed kills' is not supported by the evidence. Deaths from stimulants are rare.

Another related stimulant, MDMA (3,4-methylene-dioxymethamphetamine or ecstasy) has increased in popularity as a party drug. Its use over many hours can cause problems with fluid balance. Deaths have been reported from water overload as well as some cases of the opposite, dehydration. The drug has also been associated with hyperthermia or overheating. This is very dangerous and can cause permanent brain damage or death. Effective treatment is available for these rare eventualities, but victims must reach treatment facilities in time.

## OTHER DRUGS: LSD, MAGIC MUSHROOMS, PEYOTE

While these drugs are used less widely than in previous decades, they are more often used in a relatively controlled manner. They are generally less harmful than opiates, alcohol or tobacco. Deaths from these drugs alone are almost unknown in Australia. They are non-addictive psychedelic drugs, causing altered states of perception and hallucinations. Subjects often develop a syndrome like schizophrenia with paranoia, delusions and voices. This is usually short lived and reversible. It can sometimes be intensely unpleasant, leading to the term 'a bad trip'.

Some cases of massive LSD overdose have been reported to cause a permanent psychotic disorder. This is usually unintentional and may result from 'concentrate' being taken in place of the diluted form. The administration of large doses of anti-psychotic drugs to someone on LSD is also dangerous. This can happen if drug intoxication is mis-diagnosed as acute psychotic delirium.

Certain varieties of ground fungus have psychoactive properties. Some are deadly, so great care is taken by the users to identify them by shape, size, colour and seasonal appearance.

Peyote cactus tops contain an intoxicant which has been used by the traditional inhabitants of Mexico for hundreds of years. This practice has been adopted by some groups for recreation or as part of religious observance. The active ingredient, mescalin, produces hallucinations and mimicking schizophrenia.

## OTHER DRUGS: COCAINE

Refined from the South American coca leaf, this short acting stimulant can be injected, smoked ('free-based') or 'snorted'. In the USA cocaine is much cheaper than in Australia. This may be why cocaine deaths are still rare in Australia. Its clinical hallmark is multiple injections of the same age, often along the one vein. It is often considered a chic party drug.

In the form of leaf chewing or brewed tea, the drug is virtually harmless. Indeed, for some years it was one of the active constituents of Coca Cola and still forms part of the name. Being illegal in most countries, the bulky and safer leaf form is rarely made available outside South America, leaving only the more harmful concentrate for black market supplies.

It is certainly a 'more-ish' drug for which people beg, borrow and sometimes steal. It is considered to be non-addictive by many authorities as it has no reproducible abstinence syndrome.

It is said that Pope John-Paul II was revived by a cup of coca leaf tea when visiting high altitude areas in South America. This benign beverage may be a useful remedy for jet-lag as well as altitude sickness.

⌘

# CHRONOLOGY

1821    Publication of De Quincey's book, *Confessions of an English Opium Eater*, the first personal addiction story.

1898    Heroin first marketed by Bayer Company as a 'non-addictive drug' and a 'cure for morphinism'.

1918 to 1933  Eighteenth Amendment. US 'prohibition' period.

1935    Founding of A.A. in Ohio, USA, by Bill W and Dr Bob.

1953    Publication of *Junkie* by William S. Burroughs.

1953    Banning of heroin in Australia (against medical advice).

1961    *The Single Convention* of UN consolidated bans on non-medical use of heroin and opium in signatory countries.

1964    First official reports accept tobacco in the causation of lung cancer.

1965    First R&R personnel come to Sydney from Vietnam.

1965    Dole's report on success of methadone treatment.

1969    First Australian patients treated with methadone.

1980    First cases of HIV/AIDS recognised.

1985    Harm minimization and methadone adopted by Aust. Special Premiers Conference in strategy against HIV.

1990    Hepatitis C becomes major concern amongst drug users.

1993    Study of 150 NSW heroin related deaths shows that only 2% were currently enrolled in methadone treatment.

1995    Northern Territory becomes third jurisdiction (after ACT and SA) to decriminalise personal use of cannabis.

1996    Tobacco accepted as addictive by US President Clinton.

1996    Over 17,000 Australians on methadone treatment in all jurisdictions except Northern Territory.

1996    Over 18,000 Australians die from tobacco related illnesses.

# READING LIST

Anonymous *Go Ask Alice* Corgi 1971

Berridge, Virginia and Edwards, Griffith *Opium and the People* Yale University Press 1981

Burroughs, William *Junky* (re-issued) Penguin 1977

Crowley, Aleister *The Diary of a Drug Fiend* University Books 1970

De Quincey, Thomas *Confessions of an English Opium Eater* Penguin 1971

Faust, Beatrice *Benzo Junkie* Penguin 1993

Grinspoon, Lester *Marijuana Reconsidered* Bantam 1971

Grinspoon, Lester and Bakalar, James *Drug Control in a Free Society* Cambridge 1984

Krivanek, Jara *Addictions* Allen and Unwin 1988

Leary, Timothy *Jail Notes* Grove 1970

Manderson, Desmond *From Mr Sin to Mr Big* Oxford 1993

McCoy, Alfred *Drug Traffic* Harper and Row 1980

Trickett, Shirley *Coming off Tranquillizers and Sleeping Pills* Thorsons 1986

Trocchi, Alexander *Cain's Book* Calder 1960

Wodak, Alex and Owen, Ron. *Prohibition - A call for change* UNSW Press, 1996

# GLOSSARY

| | |
|---|---|
| *acid* | LSD |
| *barbs* | barbiturates |
| *benzo* | drug of benzodiazepine family (cf. pills) |
| *blockade* | high dose methadone (loose term) |
| *blue* | overdosed |
| *bolt* | evade police or court (often interstate) |
| *bombed* | intoxicated |
| *bombed* | (of vein) injection into the tissues (= popped) |
| *bong* | apparatus for smoking drugs through water |
| *bring down (v.)* | |
| | administer naloxone as opioid antidote |
| *can (n.)* | prison |
| *carck* | to die (Aust. coll.) |
| *chase the dragon* | |
| | (arch.) smoke heroin or opium |
| *clagged* | blocked (of vein) (= bombed, popped) |
| *crack* | smoked cocaine (not used in Australia) |
| *deal (n.)* | quantity of drug (usually for a single day's use) |
| *deal (v.)* | buy and sell drugs |
| *do doctors* | attend numerous doctors for prescriptions |
| *do chemists* | steal from pharmacies |
| *'done* | methadone |
| *downer* | sedative, usually benzodiazepine tranquillizer |
| *drop (n.)* | delivery of illicit substance |
| *drop (v.)* | to overdose |
| *earner* | robbery, cf. scam |
| *eckies* | ecstasy (3,4-methylenedioxymethamphetamine, MDMA) |

| | |
|---|---|
| *fence* | retailer of stolen property |
| *fit (n.)* | syringe and needle |
| *fix(n. arch)* | quantity of drug for immediate use |
| *freebase* | cocaine suitable for smoking i.e. 'crack' |
| *ganja* | cannabis flowering heads |
| *gear* | heroin |
| *gear* | steroids |
| *geographical (n.)* | |
| | a trip away to detoxify |
| *goey* | amphetamine |
| *grass* | cannabis |
| *hammer* | heroin |
| *hang out (v)* | to be in opioid withdrawal |
| *'hard' drug* | more dangerous drug (eg heroin and cocaine) |
| *harry* | heroin |
| *hash* | hashish (derivation disputed: cannabis resin) |
| *head* | addict or compulsive user (e.g. 'pot' head) |
| *hot shot* | contaminated injection |
| *hydro* | hydroponically grown cannabis |
| *inside* | in jail |
| *IVDU* | intravenous drug user |
| *joint* | (trad.) cannabis cigarette |
| *junkie* | (trad.) young, street heroin addict |
| *loaded up* | falsely charged with drug possession |
| *mandy* | methaqualone compound (Mandrax) |
| *MDMA* | see ecstasy |
| *moggies* | Mogadon (nitrazepam - long acting tranquillizer) |
| *Narcan* | antidote to opioid overdose, given intravenously |
| *narcotic* | equivalent to opioid (US: also refers to cocaine) |
| *nodding off* | intoxicated with heroin (cf scratching, wasted) |
| *O.D.* | overdose |
| *opioid* | synthetic or natural drug with narcotic properties, e.g. morphine, pethidine, methadone (cf. opiate) |
| *opiate* | drug which is derived from the opium poppy: codeine, heroin, morphine, papaveretum |
| *pills* | tranquillizers, usually of benzodiazepine type |

| | |
|---|---|
| *pinned out* | having pin-point pupils; opioid intoxication |
| *pot* | cannabis, marijuana, ganga |
| *qualud* | (US arch.) methaqualone tablet |
| *reefer* | (arch.) cannabis cigarette |
| *ripped* | intoxicated (= stoned) |
| *Rivotril* | clonazepam, abused anti-convulsant (cf. benzo.) |
| *roach* | (arch.) butt of cannabis cigarette |
| *rock* | purest forms of heroin, e.g. pink r.; Bangkok r. |
| *row-ees* | Rohypnol tablets (flunitrazepam, Roche) |
| *scag* | (arch.) heroin |
| *scam* | robbery or set-up |
| *score (v.)* | obtain illicit drug (usually heroin or cocaine) |
| *scratching* | opiate intoxication (involuntary body scratching) |
| *screws* | prison wardens |
| *sera's* | Serepax (oxazepam) |
| *shit* | heroin |
| *snort* | intra-nasal insufflation (cocaine or heroin) |
| *snowcone* | cannabis bong with added cocaine or heroin |
| *'soft' drug* | less dangerous drug (eg cannabis or ecstasy) |
| *speed* | amphetamine or metamphetamine |
| *speedball* | heroin and cocaine combination |
| *stoned* | intoxicated |
| *thrombosis* | vein which is clotted or infected |
| *tolerance* | the property of getting less effect with same dose |
| *tracks* | venipunctures, injection marks |
| *trip (1)* | episode on hallucinogen, usually LSD |
| *trip (2)* | voyage to obtain drugs (usually to Asia) |
| *'uppa'* | stimulant drug (e.g. amphetamine) |
| *wasted* | severely intoxicated (usually from heroin) |
| *weed* | cannabis |
| *'weight'* | dealer's "gram" of heroin (usually much less) |
| *white lady* | mixture of milk and methylated spirits |
| *work (v.)* | prostitution (male or female) |
| *works (n.pl.)* | needle, syringe, spoon, tourniquet and swabs |
| *yawning* | in opioid withdrawal |

## REFERENCES:

[1] Dole VP, Nyswander ME. A medical treatment for diacetylmorphine (heroin) addiction. *JAMA* 1965; 193: 646

[2] Ward J, Mattick RP, Hall W. *Key Issues In Methadone Maintenance Treatment*, 1992. NSW University Press.

[3] D'Aunno T, Vaughan TE. Variations in methadone treatment practices; results from a national study. *JAMA* 1992; 267: 253.

[4] Ball J, Ross A: The Effectiveness of Methadone Maintenance Treatment. Springer-Verlag, New York 1986.

[5] Zador D, Lyons Wall PM, Webster I. High sugar intake in a group of women on methadone maintenance in South Western Sydney, Australia. *Addiction* (1996) 91 (7), 1053-61

[6] Novick DM, Richman BL, Friedman JM, Friedman JE, Wilson JP, Townley A, Kreek MJ. The medical status of methadone maintenance patients in treatment for 11-18 years. *Drug and Alcohol Dependence*, 33 1993:235-245.

[7] Newman RG, What's so special about methadone maintenance? 1991 *Drug and Alcohol Review* 10: 225-232.

[8] Hartnoll RL, Mitchelson MC, Battersby A, Brown G, Ellis M, Fleming P, Hedley N. Evaluation of Heroin Maintenance in Controlled Trial. *Archives of General Psychiatry* 1980 37:877

[9] Thorley A. Longitudinal Studies of Drug Dependance. In: *Drug Problems in Britain: A review of ten years*. Eds: Edwards G, Busch C. 1981, Academic Press. p162

[10] Gearing FR, Schweitzer MD. An epidemiologic evaluation of long-term methadone maintenance treatment for heroin addiction. *American Journal of Epidemiology* 1974; 100: 101

[11] Grönbladh L, Öhlund LS, Gunne LM. Mortality in heroin addiction: impact of methadone treatment. *Acta Psychiatrica Scand* 1990; 82: 223 - 227

[12] Zador D, Sunjic S, Darke S. Heroin-related deaths in New South Wales, 1992: toxicological findings and circumstances. *Medical Journal of Australia* 1996; 164: 204-7.

[13] van Brussel G. Methadone Treatment by GPs in Amsterdam. *Bulletin of the New York Academy of Medicine* 1995.72:2;348.

## *ABOUT THE AUTHOR ...*

Andrew Byrne is a third generation medical practitioner from Sydney. Following six years working in inner city hospitals, he commenced general practice where he first treated drug addicts in 1984. He was the first general practitioner in New South Wales approved to prescribe methadone for addiction and has treated up to 130 patients at a time for over ten years.

He studied methadone treatment facilities in New York, San Francisco, Brighton (England) and Hong Kong. His successful rehabilitation strategy is based on the medical model originally proposed by Dr Vincent P. Dole in 1965.

The general practice setting has permitted observation of long-term outcomes in patients who have completed methadone treatment. Dr Byrne presented his practice profile to the European *THS-3* Conference in Cannes in 1995.

His book, *Methadone in the Treatment of Narcotic Addiction*, was one of the first texts written on the subject. It was well received both in Australia and overseas. Dr Byrne is also widely published on various drug and alcohol issues including the use of nicotine patches, benzodiazepine addiction as well as politically viable alternatives to the prohibition of drugs.

His other interests include Early Dynastic Egypt, the pianoforte and bel canto opera.

### Recent Scientific Publications:

'Census of patients receiving methadone treatment in a general practice'. *Addiction Research* 1996 3:4;341 (with Dr A. Wodak).

'Ten patients prescribed high dose methadone maintenance in general practice'. *Medical Journal of Australia* 1996:165;239.

'Use of dextromoramide to stabilize a heroin addict'. *Drug and Alcohol Review* 1996; 15: 200.

'Methadone syrup causes dental decay'. *Australian Dental Journal*. 1996 41:1;61.

'Problem Drug Users'. *Brit Journ Gen Pract*. March 1996:200.

# ORDER FORM FOR FURTHER COPIES

*Name* _____

*Address* _____

_____

_____

_____ *Code*_____

*Please send me* _____*copies of "Addict in the Family".*

*Enclosed is a cheque for $A_____, being $13 per copy (Australian currency) plus postage and handling (1 or 2 copies: $3 [$4 overseas]; 3 or more copies: $10 flat rate).*

*or, please bill $A_____to Mastercard/Visa/Bankcard in above name, credit card number:*

._____._____._____._____.

*expiry date: ___/___*

*Signature:_____*

*Please photocopy this page and post or fax to:*

*Tosca Press,*
*75 Redfern St, Redfern, NSW, 2016, Australia*
*Fax: 61 2 9318 0631*

*Also available: "Methadone in the Treatment of Narcotic Addiction" 96pp. $30 inc. postage.*

# INDEX